LATIN'S NOT SO TOUGH!

LEVEL THREE

A Classical Latin Worktext
by
Karen Mohs

Dear Parent/Teacher:

Welcome to the Latin Workbook Level Three!

In this workbook, students review the Latin alphabet and vocabulary introduced in Levels One and Two. They then construct simple sentences as they learn to use the specialized endings on nouns and verbs.

Remove the flashcard pages at the end of the workbook, cut out the words, and copy, paste, or tape them onto 3 by 5 inch cards.

Begin use of flashcards on page 11 of the workbook. Your student should put a check mark in the box at the bottom of each page when daily flashcard work is completed. Please refer to "Flashcard Tips" in the appendix.

A glossary and paradigms for the conjugation and declensions taught in this workbook are included for those who would find such resources helpful. An answer key is available, as well as quizzes/exams, flashcards on a ring, and an audio pronunciation CD or cassette tape.

References for this series include *First Year Latin* by Charles Jenney, Jr., *Second Year Latin* by Charles Jenney, Jr., and *The New College Latin & English Dictionary* by John C. Traupman, Ph.D.

Keep having fun!

Copyright © 1998 by Karen Mohs
All rights reserved. No part of this publication may be reproduced without prior permission of the author.

ISBN-13: 978-1-931842-60-0
ISBN-10: 1-931842-60-4

Greek 'n' Stuff
P.O. Box 882
Moline, IL 61266-0882
www.greeknstuff.com

Revised 9/04

This workbook belongs to me:

_____

(student's name)

because
I'M LEARNING LATIN
Level Three!

TABLE OF CONTENTS

+ review
C1-2
CC Latin

Latin Workbook - Level 3
Copyright © 1998 by Karen Mohs

Appendix

LET'S REVIEW THE LATIN ALPHABET

Ā ā

As you write the letters across each line, say the sound of "a" in *father*.

Ā ā – – – – – – –

As you write the letters across each line, say the sound of "a" in *idea*.

A a – – – – – – –

A a

B b

As you write the letters across each line, say the sound of "b" in *boy*.

B b – – – – – – –

As you write the letters across each line, say the sound of "c" in *cat*.

C c – – – – – – –

C c

D d

As you write the letters across each line, say the sound of "d" in *dog*.

D d – – – – – – –

As you write the letters across each line, say the sound of "ey" in *obey*.

Ē ē – – – – – – –

Ē ē

MORE LATIN ALPHABET REVIEW

As you write the letters across each line, say the sound of "e" in *bet*.

E e

E e

As you write the letters across each line, say the sound of "f" in *fan*.

F f

F f

As you write the letters across each line, say the sound of "g" in *go*.

G g

G g

As you write the letters across each line, say the sound of "h" in *hat*.

H h

H h

As you write the letters across each line, say the sound of "i" in *machine*.

Ī ī

Ī ī

As you write the letters across each line, say the sound of "i" in *sit*.

I i

I i

MORE LATIN ALPHABET REVIEW

K k

As you write the letters across each line, say the sound of "**k**" in *king*.

K k

As you write the letters across each line, say the sound of "**l**" in *land*.

L l

L l

M m

As you write the letters across each line, say the sound of "**m**" in *man*.

M m

As you write the letters across each line, say the sound of "**n**" in *nut*.

N n

N n

Ō ō

As you write the letters across each line, say the sound of "**o**" in *note*.*

Ō ō

As you write the letters across each line, say the sound of "**o**" in *omit*.*

O o

O o

*Although both Latin "o" sounds are "long," the ō as in *note* is held longer than the o as in *omit*.

MORE LATIN ALPHABET REVIEW

As you write the letters across each line, say the sound of "**p**" in *pit*.

P p

As you write the letters across each line, say the sound of "**qu**" in *quit*.

Q q

Qu qu

As you write the letters across each line, say the sound of "**r**" in *run*.

R r

R r

S s

As you write the letters across each line, say the sound of "**s**" in *sit*.

S s

As you write the letters across each line, say the sound of "**t**" in *tag*.

T t

T t

Ū ū

As you write the letters across each line, say the sound of "**u**" in *rule*.

Ū ū

4

MORE LATIN ALPHABET REVIEW

U u

As you write the letters across each line, say the sound of "**u**" in *put*.

Ū u – – – – – – – – – – – –

As you write the letters across each line, say the sound of "**w**" in *way*.

V v – – – – – – – – – – – –

V v

X x

As you write the letters across each line, say the sound of "**ks**" in *socks*.

X x – – – – – – – – – – – –

As you write the letters across each line, form your lips to say "**oo**" but say "**ee**" instead. (Hold the sound longer than Latin y.)

Ȳ ȳ – – – – – – – – – – – –

Ȳ ȳ

Y y

As you write the letters across each line, form your lips to say "**oo**" but say "**ee**" instead. (Hold the sound shorter than Latin ȳ.)

Y y – – – – – – – – – – – –

As you write the letters across each line, say the sound of "**dz**" in *adze*.

Z z – – – – – – – – – – – –

Z z

MORE LATIN ALPHABET REVIEW

Match the letters to their sounds.

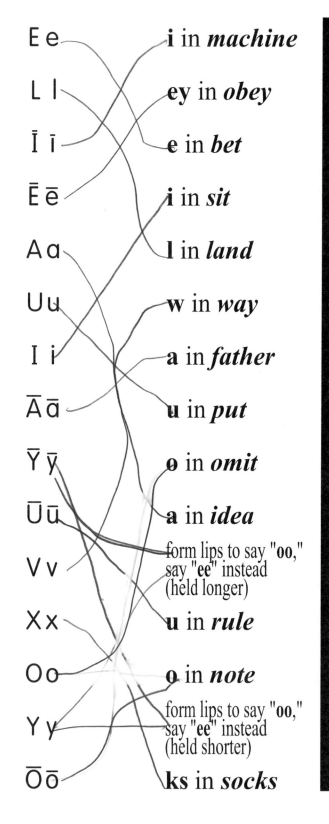

E e	**i** in *machine*
L l	**ey** in *obey*
Ī ī	**e** in *bet*
Ē ē	**i** in *sit*
A a	**l** in *land*
U u	**w** in *way*
I i	**a** in *father*
Ā ā	**u** in *put*
Ȳ ȳ	**o** in *omit*
Ū ū	**a** in *idea*
	form lips to say "oo," say "ee" instead (held longer)
V v	**u** in *rule*
X x	**o** in *note*
O o	
Y y	form lips to say "oo," say "ee" instead (held shorter)
Ō ō	**ks** in *socks*

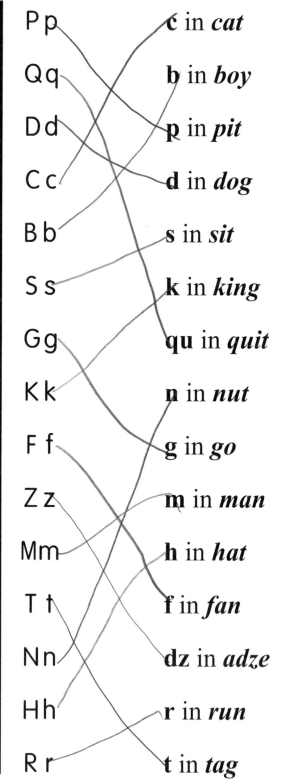

P p	**c** in *cat*
Q q	**b** in *boy*
D d	**p** in *pit*
C c	**d** in *dog*
B b	**s** in *sit*
S s	**k** in *king*
G g	**qu** in *quit*
K k	**n** in *nut*
F f	**g** in *go*
Z z	**m** in *man*
M m	**h** in *hat*
T t	**f** in *fan*
N n	**dz** in *adze*
H h	**r** in *run*
R r	**t** in *tag*

6

LET'S REVIEW LATIN DIPHTHONGS

ae

As you write the diphthong ae, say the "*aye*" sound.

ae

As you write the diphthong au, say the "**ow**" sound in *now*.

au

au

ei

As you write the diphthong ei, say the "**ei**" sound in *neighbor*.

ei

As you write the diphthong eu, say "*ay-oo*" as one syllable.

eu

eu

oe

As you write the diphthong oe, say the "**oy**" sound in *joy*.

oe

As you write the diphthong ui, say the "**uee**" sound in *queen*.

ui

ui

MORE REVIEW

Color the ball and bat if the letters on the ball make the sound on the bat.

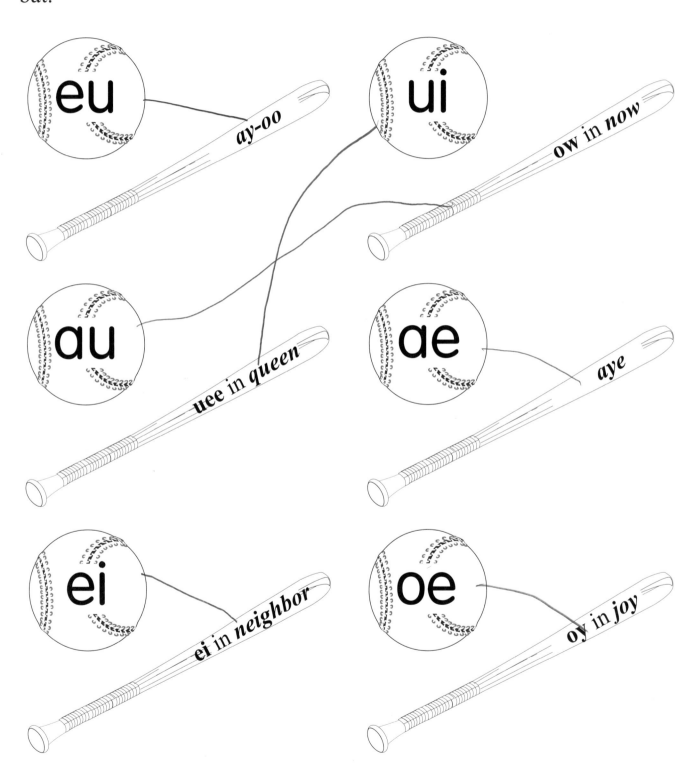

Latin Workbook - Level 3
Copyright © 1998 by Karen Mohs

LET'S REVIEW SPECIAL CONSONANT SOUNDS

bs

As you write the consonants bs, say the "*ps*" sound.

bs

As you write the consonants bt, say the "*pt*" sound.

bt

bt

ch

As you write the consonants ch, say the "**ch**" sound in *character*.

ch

As you write the consonants gu, say the "**gu**" sound in *anguish*.

gu*am*

gu

i

As you write the consonant i, say the "**y**" sound in *youth*.

i

As you write the consonants ph, say the "**ph**" sound in *phone*.

ph

ph

su

As you write the consonants su, say the "**su**" sound in *suave*.

su

As you write the consonants th, say the "**th**" sound in *thick*.

th

th

MORE REVIEW

Write the Latin letters for each sound.

1. Latin _____au_____ sounds like **ow** in *now*.

2. Latin _____eu_____ sounds like *ay-oo* (in one syllable).

3. Latin _____th_____ sounds like **th** in *thick*.

4. Latin _____ph_____ sounds like **ph** in *phone*.

5. Latin _____gu_____ sounds like **gu** in *anguish*.

6. Latin _____su_____ sounds like **su** in *suave*.

7. Latin _____pt_____ sounds like *pt*.

8. Latin _____qi_____ sounds like **uee** in *queen*.

9. Latin _____ch_____ sounds like **ch** in *character*.

10. Latin _____yi_____ sounds like **y** in *youth*.

11. Latin _____ae_____ sounds like *aye*.

12. Latin _____ps_____ sounds like *ps*.

10

Latin Workbook - Level 3
Copyright © 1998 by Karen Mohs

VOCABULARY REVIEW

puella
means
girl

Write the Latin word that means **girl**.

_____

_____

_____

Write the Latin word that means **I call**.

_____

_____

_____

vocō
means
I call

puer
means
boy

Write the Latin word that means **boy**.

_____

_____

_____

Write the Latin word that means **I give**.

_____

_____

_____

dō
means
**I give,
I grant**

Start your flashcard deck with these cards. (See back of workbook.)
☐ I practiced my flashcards today.

VOCABULARY REVIEW

Write the Latin word that means **farmer**.

_____

_____

_____

agricola

means
farmer

aqua

means
water

Write the Latin word that means **water**.

_____

_____

_____

Write the Latin word that means **he is**.

_____

_____

_____

est

means
**he is, she is,
it is, there is**

fēmina

means
**woman,
wife**

Write the Latin word that means **woman**.

_____

_____

_____

☐ I practiced my flashcards today. (Add the new cards.)

12

VOCABULARY REVIEW

et

means
**and, also,
even**

Write the Latin word that means **and**.

_____

_____

Write the Latin word that means **forest**.

_____

_____

silva

means
forest

īnsula

means
island

Write the Latin word that means **island**.

_____

_____

Write the Latin word that means **they are**.

_____

_____

sunt

means
**they are,
there are**

☐ I practiced my flashcards today. (Add the new cards.)

VOCABULARY REVIEW

Write the Latin word that means **I praise**.

_____

laud**ō**
ow

means
I praise

---

nōn

means
not

Write the Latin word that means **not**.

_____

Write the Latin word that means **to**.

_____

ad
uh

means
to, near, toward, for, at

---

vīta

means
life

Write the Latin word that means **life**.

_____

☐ I practiced my flashcards today. (Add the new cards.)

Latin Workbook - Level 3
Copyright © 1998 by Karen Mohs

VOCABULARY REVIEW

porta

means

gate

Write the Latin word that means **gate**.

_____

_____

Write the Latin word that means **memory**.

_____

_____

memoria

means

memory

nāvigō

means

I sail

Write the Latin word that means **I sail**.

_____

_____

Write the Latin word that means **but**.

_____

_____

sed

means

but

☐ I practiced my flashcards today. (Add the new cards.)

VOCABULARY REVIEW

Write the Latin word that means **fortune**.

_____
- - - - - - - - - - - - - - - - -
_____
_____
- - - - - - - - - - - - - - - - -
_____

fortūna

means
**fortune,
chance, luck**

"w"
via

means
**road, way,
street**

Write the Latin word that means **way**.

_____
- - - - - - - - - - - - - - - - -
_____
_____
- - - - - - - - - - - - - - - - -
_____

Write the Latin word that means **I carry**.

_____
- - - - - - - - - - - - - - - - -
_____
_____
- - - - - - - - - - - - - - - - -
_____

portō

means
I carry

"ṷee"
quid

means
what
(a question)

Write the Latin word that means **what?**

_____
- - - - - - - - - - - - - - - - -
_____
_____
- - - - - - - - - - - - - - - - -
_____

☐ I practiced my flashcards today. (Add the new cards.)

VOCABULARY REVIEW

tuba
means
trumpet

Write the Latin word that means **trumpet**.

_____

_____

_____

Write the Latin word that means **field**.

_____

_____

_____

ager
means
**field,
territory**

parō
means
**I prepare,
I prepare for**

Write the Latin word that means **I prepare**.

_____

_____

_____

Write the Latin word that means **friend**.

_____

_____

_____

ee
amīcus
means
friend

☐ I practiced my flashcards today. (Add the new cards.)

VOCABULARY REVIEW

Write the Latin words.

I carry	Portō	farmer	agricola
island	Insula	he is	est
friend	amīcus	woman	fēmina
life	Vita	I give	dō
there are	sunt	I sail	navigō
not	non	but	sed
I prepare	Parō	I call	vocō
territory	ager	even	et
toward	ad	memory	memoria
road	Via	what?	quid
gate	Porta	I praise	laudō
chance	fortūna	trumpet	tuba

☐ I practiced my flashcards today.

18

VOCABULARY REVIEW

spectō

means
I look at

Write the Latin word that means **I look at**.

_____

- - - - - - - - - - - - - - - - -

_____
_____

- - - - - - - - - - - - - - - - -

_____

Write the Latin word that means **nature**.

_____

- - - - - - - - - - - - - - - - -

_____
_____

- - - - - - - - - - - - - - - - -

_____

nātūra

means
nature

campus

means
**field,
plain**

Write the Latin word that means **field**.

_____

- - - - - - - - - - - - - - - - -

_____
_____

- - - - - - - - - - - - - - - - -

_____

Write the Latin word that means **I seize**.

_____

- - - - - - - - - - - - - - - - -

_____
_____

- - - - - - - - - - - - - - - - -

_____

occupō

means
**I seize,
I capture**

☐ I practiced my flashcards today. (Add the new cards.)

VOCABULARY REVIEW

Write the Latin word that means **with**.

_____

cum

means
**along with,
with**

---

nauta

means
sailor

Write the Latin word that means **sailor**.

_____

Write the Latin word that means **farmhouse**.

_____

vīlla

means
**farmhouse,
country house, villa**

---

littera

means
letter (of the alphabet),
(if plural: **epistle, letter**)

Write the Latin word that means **letter**.

_____

☐ I practiced my flashcards today. (Add the new cards.)

VOCABULARY REVIEW

ubi
means
where
(a question)

Write the Latin word that means **where?**

Write the Latin word that means **son**.

fīlius
means
son

patria
means
**country,
native land**

Write the Latin word that means **country**.

Write the Latin word that means **daughter**.

fīlia
means
daughter

☐ I practiced my flashcards today. (Add the new cards.)

VOCABULARY REVIEW

Write the Latin word that means **friendship**.

_____

amīcitia

means
**friendliness,
friendship**

amō

means
**I love,
I like**

Write the Latin word that means **I love**.

_____

Write the Latin word that means **tongue**.

_____

lingua

means
**tongue,
language**

equus

means
horse

Write the Latin word that means **horse**.

_____

☐ I practiced my flashcards today. (Add the new cards.)

VOCABULARY REVIEW

poēta

means
poet

Write the Latin word that means **poet**.

_____

_____

Write the Latin word that means **year**.

_____

_____

annus

means
year

pugnō

means
I fight

Write the Latin word that means **I fight**.

_____

_____

Write the Latin word that means **earth**.

_____

_____

terra

means
**earth, land,
country**

☐ I practiced my flashcards today. (Add the new cards.)

VOCABULARY REVIEW

Write the Latin word that means **sword**.

————————————————————————————
– – – – – – – – – – – – – – – – – – – –
————————————————————————————
– – – – – – – – – – – – – – – – – – – –
————————————————————————————

gladius
means
sword

prōvincia
means
province

Write the Latin word that means **province**.

————————————————————————————
– – – – – – – – – – – – – – – – – – – –
————————————————————————————
– – – – – – – – – – – – – – – – – – – –
————————————————————————————

Circle **yes** or **no**.

yes no	1.	Aqua is a Latin word that means **blue**.
yes no	2.	Puer is a Latin word that means **boy**.
yes no	3.	Fortūna is a Latin word that means **luck**.
yes no	4.	Patria is a Latin word that means **country**.
yes no	5.	Tuba is a Latin word that means **straw**.
yes no	6.	Lingua is a Latin word that means **language**.
yes no	7.	Vīta is a Latin word that means **pill**.
yes no	8.	Nauta is a Latin word that means **bad**.

☐ I practiced my flashcards today. (Add the new cards.)

VOCABULARY REVIEW

Match the words to their meanings.

cum	sword	via	not
gladius	along with	nāvigō	I carry
fīlius	horse	nōn	street
equus	I like	laudō	I praise
vocō	son	portō	I sail
amīcus	I call	patria	year
amō	she is	silva	girl
est	friend	annus	native land
quid	where?	puella	forest
pugnō	what?	aqua	island
ubi	territory	vīta	tongue
puer	I fight	lingua	life
ager	poet	īnsula	water
poēta	gate	sunt	nature
porta	boy	nātūra	they are

☐ I practiced my flashcards today.

VOCABULARY REVIEW

Write the Latin words.

son _____	poet _____
where? _____	sailor _____
girl _____	friendship _____
plain _____	nature _____
earth _____	year _____
I look at _____	villa _____
daughter _____	horse _____
sword _____	water _____
letter _____	I fight _____
language _____	with _____
I love _____	province _____
forest _____	I seize _____

☐ I practiced my flashcards today.

> Amō puellam.*   It means **I like the girl.**
>
> Amō fīlium.   It means **I like the son.**

Now read these Latin sentences. Write what they mean.

1. Amō nautam.

   It means _____

2. Amō vīllam.

   It means _____

3. Spectō equum.

   It means _____

4. Laudō amīcum.

   It means _____

Put a check in the box when you notice:

☐ The last letters of the words fīlius, equus, and amīcus changed from us to um.

☐ The last letters of the words puella, nauta, and vīlla changed from a to am.

Endings of Latin words change when the words are used in different parts of the sentence. We will learn more about this later.

*This third level uses an *inductive* ("parts to whole") approach. See the paradigms in the appendix for the "whole" picture. Level Four transitions to a *deductive* ("whole to parts") approach.

☐ I practiced my flashcards today. (Add the new cards.)

LET'S PRACTICE

Circle the correct Latin words. Then write what the sentences mean.

1. Vocō puellam.
   puella.

   It means _____

2. Gladius dō.*
   Gladium

   It means _____

3. Pugnō agricola.
   agricolam.

   It means _____

4. Parō equuum.
   equus.

   It means _____

Fill in the blanks with the correct Latin words.

_____

1. _____ campum.
   (I look at)

2. Portō _____.
   (the daughter)

3. _____ occupō.
   (the forest)

*Notice that word order in Latin is not the same as word order in English. In Latin, since the ending tells us what part the word plays in the sentence, word order is used for emphasis. However, there is a tendency to place the verb last.

[ ] I practiced my flashcards today.

Latin Workbook - Level 3
Copyright © 1998 by Karen Mohs

LET'S PRACTICE

Choose the correct words for the sentences. Put them in the blanks. Then write what the sentences mean.

| Fēminam - Fēmina |

1. _____ laudō.

It means _____

| tuba - tubam |

2. Spectō _____ .

It means _____

| Nauta - Nautam |

3. _____ pugnō.

It means _____

| Fīliam - Fīlia |

4. _____ portō.

It means _____

| equus - equum |

5. Vocō _____ .

It means _____

| Aquam - Aqua |

6. _____ amō.

It means _____

| Fīlius - Fīlium |

7. _____ occupō.

It means _____

☐ I practiced my flashcards today.

LET'S PRACTICE

Connect each raindrop to the correct puddle.

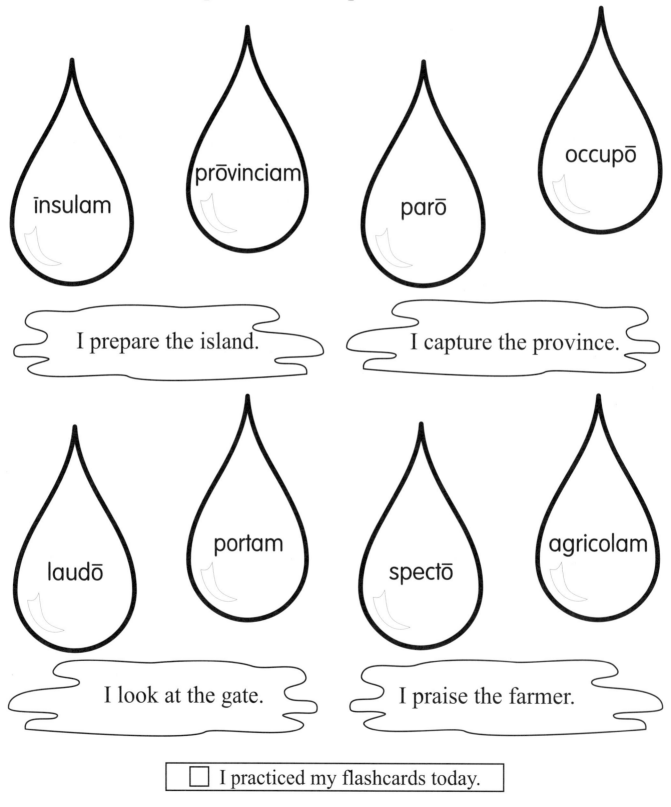

insulam

prōvinciam

parō

occupō

I prepare the island.

I capture the province.

laudō

portam

spectō

agricolam

I look at the gate.

I praise the farmer.

☐ I practiced my flashcards today.

Puellam amō.	It means **I like the girl.**
Puellās amō.	It means **I like the *girls*.**
Nautam amō.	It means **I like the sailor.**
Nautās amō.	It means **I like the *sailors*.**

Fill in the blanks with am or ās.

The ending _____ changes to the ending _____ when the word means more than one.

Fīlium amō.	It means **I like the son.**
Fīliōs amō.	It means **I like the *sons*.**
Campum amo.	It means **I like the plain.**
Campōs amō.	It means **I like the *plains*.**

Fill in the blanks with um or ōs.

The ending _____ changes to the ending _____ when the word means more than one.

☐ I practiced my flashcards today. (Add the new cards.)

LET'S PRACTICE

Match the Latin sentences to their meanings.

_____ 1. Gladiōs portō.   a. I love the daughters.

_____ 2. Fīliās amō.   b. I fight the poet.

_____ 3. Vocō poētās.   c. I carry the swords.

_____ 4. Poētam pugnō.   d. I like the friendship.

_____ 5. Amō amīcitiam.   e. I call the poets.

_____ 6. Terram occupō.   f. I prepare the way.

_____ 7. Dō litterās.   g. I look at the letter.

_____ 8. Viam parō.   h. I praise the native land.

_____ 9. Patriam laudō.   i. I give the epistle.

_____ 10. Litteram spectō.   j. I seize the land.

Circle the Latin sentence that means:

I love the sons and the friend.

1. Amō fīlius et amīcus.

2. Fīliōs et amīcum amō.

3. Fīliōs et amīcās amō.

☐ I practiced my flashcards today.

LET'S PRACTICE

Write the sentences using the words on the right.

1. _____

   It means **I carry the trumpets.**

2. _____

   It means **I look at friends.**

3. _____

   It means **I prepare for life.**

| amīcōs |
| parō |
| portō |
| spectō |
| tubās |
| vītam |

Fill in the missing letters on the Latin words.

1. Agricol_____ voc_____, et amō fili_____.
   It means **I call the farmer, and I like the daughter.**

2. Puell_____ et gladi_____ laudō.
   It means **I praise the girls and the swords.**

3. D_____ silv_____, et portō equ_____.
   It means **I give the forests, and I carry the horses.**

[ ] I practiced my flashcards today.

LET'S PRACTICE

Draw pictures for these sentences.

Puellam et gladiōs portō.

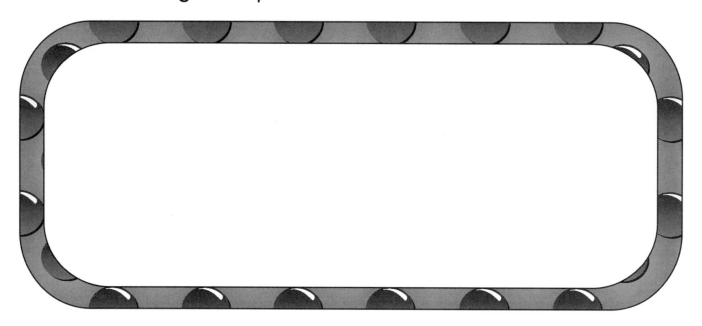

Puellās et gladium portō.

☐ I practiced my flashcards today.

Puellam amō.   It means **I like the girl.**
Puellam amāmus.   It means *We* **like the girl.**

Puellam portō.   It means **I carry the girl.**
Puellam portāmus.   It means *We* **carry the girl.**

Fill in the blank with either ō or āmus.

If I want to say *I* do something, I use the ending _____.

If I want to say *we* do something, I use the ending _____.

Match the Latin words to their meanings.

parāmus	I sail
parō	we prepare for
nāvigō	we sail
nāvigāmus	I prepare for

Read the Latin sentences. Write what they mean.

1. Occupāmus campōs, sed occupō viam.

   It means _____

2. Pugnō poētam, et pugnāmus filiās.

   It means _____

☐ I practiced my flashcards today. (Add the new cards.)

LET'S PRACTICE

Circle the correct Latin words.

I carry		memories	
laudō	portāmus	īnsulās	equōs
parō	portō	memoriam	memoriās
fortunes		**life**	
linguās	fortūnam	vītam	vīllās
fortūnās	prōvinciās	vītās	viās
we sail		**we love**	
nāvigāmus	nāvigō	amō	amāmus
occupāmus	portāmus	laudāmus	occupō
nature		**I look at**	
silvam	nātūrās	parō	spectō
nautās	nātūram	spectāmus	nāvigō
I call		**years**	
vocāmus	pugnō	patriam	annum
vocō	laudāmus	litteram	annōs
friendliness		**I grant**	
amīcitiās	amīcitiam	dō	parāmus
amīcum	amīcōs	vocō	laudō

☐ I practiced my flashcards today.

LET'S PRACTICE

Circle the correct meanings of the Latin sentences.

Silvās spectāmus.	I look at the forests. I look at the forest. We look at the forests.
Portō litterās.	You carry the epistle. I carry the epistle. We carry the epistle.
Puellās amō.	I love the girls. I love the girl. We love the girl.
Spectō vīllam.	We look at the farmhouse. I look at the farmhouses. I look at the farmhouse.
Portāmus portās.	You carry the gates. We carry the gates. I carry the gate.
Dō gladium.	I give the sword. He gives the sword. We give the swords.

☐ I practiced my flashcards today.

LET'S PRACTICE

Color the book blue if the word means only one. Color the book green if the word means more than one.

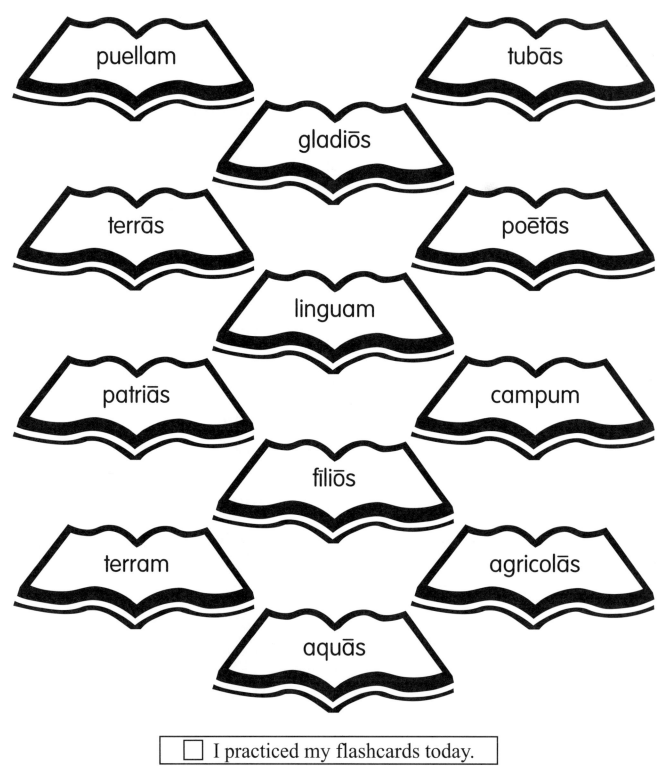

puellam

tubās

gladiōs

terrās

poētās

linguam

patriās

campum

fīliōs

terram

agricolās

aquās

☐ I practiced my flashcards today.

Latin Workbook - Level 3
Copyright © 1998 by Karen Mohs

Vīllam amō.

It means **I like the farmhouse.**

Vīllam puellae amō.

It means **I like the farmhouse *of the girl.***
or
I like the *girl's* farmhouse.

The new ending is **ae**. It replaces the **a** at the end of words like **puella** to show that the farmhouse belongs to the girl.

Vīllam filī amō.

It means **I like the farmhouse *of the son.***
or
I like the *son's* farmhouse.

Vīllam amīcī amō.

It means **I like the farmhouse *of the friend.***
or
I like the *friend's* farmhouse.

The new ending is **ī**. It replaces the **ius** at the end of words like **filius** (or the **us** at the end of words like **amīcus**) to show that the farmhouse belongs to the son (or to the friend).

Fill in the blank with either **ae** or **ī** to show something belongs.

If the word ends like **puella**, change the **a** to _____.

If the word ends like **filius**, change the **ius** to _____.

If the word ends like **amīcus**, change the **us** to _____.

| ☐ I practiced my flashcards today. (Add the new cards.) |

LET'S PRACTICE

Circle the correct Latin words. Then write what the sentences mean.

1. Gladius / Gladiōs nautae portō.

   It means _____

2. Vocāmus equum / equus fīlī.

   It means _____

3. Fīlia / Fīliam fēminae pugnō.

   It means _____

4. Annōs / Annus amīcitiae amāmus.

   It means _____

Match the correct Latin sentences to their meanings below.

a. Viās terrae laudō.   d. Nautās et agricolās vocō.

b. Litterās poētae amō.   e. Nautās et agricolās vocāmus.

c. Viās terrae spectāmus.   f. Litteram poētae dō.

_____ 1. We look at the roads of the land.

_____ 2. I love the poet's letter.

_____ 3. I praise the roads of the land.

_____ 4. We call the sailors and the farmers.

☐ I practiced my flashcards today.

LET'S PRACTICE

Choose the correct words for the sentences. Put them in the blanks.
Then write what the sentences mean.

| nautae - nauta |

1. Fīlium _____ amāmus.

    It means _____

| agricola - agricolae |

2. Pugnō equum _____.

    It means _____

| tubam - tuba |

3. Portō puellae _____.

    It means _____

| Silva - Silvam |

4. _____ fēminae occupāmus.

    It means _____

| patriae - patria |

5. Aquam laudāmus _____.

    It means _____

| Puella - Puellās |

6. _____ et fēminās vocō.

    It means _____

| Gladius - Gladiōs |

7. _____ prōvinciae spectō.

    It means _____

☐ I practiced my flashcards today.

LET'S PRACTICE

Draw a smile on the chef's face if the word on his hat matches the meaning on his bow tie. Draw a frown if the meanings do not match.

I practiced my flashcards today.

lēgātus

means

lieutenant, envoy

Write the Latin word that means **envoy**.

Write the Latin word that means **game**.

lūdus

means

game, play, school

appellō

means

I address, I call, I name

Write the Latin word that means **I address**.

☐ I practiced my flashcards today. (Add the new cards.)

LET'S PRACTICE

Color the box blue if the English meaning matches the Latin word at the beginning of the row.

cum	along with	I go	but
appellāmus	I name	we name	you name
lūdī	of the school	of schools	school
lēgātus	lieutenants	court	lieutenant
memoriās	of memories	memories	memory
appellō	he calls	I address	you name
lēgātī	courts	of the court	of the envoy
quid	what?	who?	why?
nāvigāmus	they sail	she sails	we sail
nātūrās	natures	shoes	beauty

☐ I practiced my flashcards today.

servus

means

slave

Write the Latin word that means **slave**.

_____

_____

_____

_____

Write the Latin word that means **message**.

_____

_____

_____

_____

nūntius

means

**messenger,
message, news**

nūntiō

means

**I announce,
I report**

Write the Latin word that means **I report**.

_____

_____

_____

_____

☐ I practiced my flashcards today. (Add the new cards.)

LET'S PRACTICE

Circle the correct Latin words.

we prepare for		of the memory	
pugnāmus	patriās	īnsula	vīta
portāmus	parāmus	equī	memoriae
messengers		**I praise**	
nātūrae	poētam	laudō	lēgātōs
nūntiōs	nautam	linguam	lēgātum
of the water		**I grant**	
aquae	amīcitiae	gladī	dō
annī	amīcum	fortūnae	portam
message		**year**	
nūntium	nātūra	amīcī	annum
memoria	nūntī	amāmus	terram
we report		**language**	
parō	nūntius	lingua	lūdum
nūntiāmus	nūntiō	lūdus	littera
of the slave		**schools**	
servum	servus	lūdōs	linguae
servī	servōs	litterae	campum

☐ I practiced my flashcards today.

nārrō

means

**I relate,
I tell**

Write the Latin word that means **I relate**.

Write the Latin word that means **rumor**.

fāma

means

**report, rumor,
reputation**

---

populus*

means

**people, nation,
tribe**

Write the Latin word that means **people**.

*Populus is usually singular. If plural, it means *nations* or *tribes*.

☐ I practiced my flashcards today. (Add the new cards.)

LET'S PRACTICE

Choose the correct words for the sentences. Put them in the blanks.
Then write what the sentences mean.

| populī - populus |

1. Memoriam nārrō _____.

It means _____

| fāmās - fāmae |

2. Nūntiāmus _____ servī.

It means _____

| viae - viam |

3. Vīllam et _____ spectāmus.

It means _____

| Populum - Populus |

4. _____ nūntī pugnō.

It means _____

| fortūna - fortūnās |

5. Fīliae _____ nārrāmus.

It means _____

| īnsula - īnsulae |

6. Poētās _____ amō.

It means _____

| lēgātī - lēgātōs |

7. Fīliōs appellāmus _____.

It means _____

| ☐ I practiced my flashcards today. |

48

rēgīna means **queen**	Write the Latin word that means **queen**. _____ _____ _____ _____ _____

Write the Latin word that means **I await**.

_____
_____
_____
_____

	exspectō means **I await,** **I wait for**

epistula means **letter,** **epistle**	Write the Latin word that means **letter**. _____ _____ _____ _____ _____

☐ I practiced my flashcards today. (Add the new cards.)

LET'S PRACTICE

Write the meanings of these Latin words.

servī _____	rēgīnam _____
fīliam _____	silvās _____
exspectō _____	patria _____
tubās _____	occupō _____
vītās _____	nātūrae _____
populus _____	lūdus _____
epistula _____	fāma _____
rēgīnae _____	amīcōs _____
vocāmus _____	amāmus _____
tubam _____	nātūram _____
parāmus _____	terra _____
campōs _____	damus _____
rēgīnās _____	puellam _____
patriam _____	silvae _____
gladī _____	īnsulās _____

☐ I practiced my flashcards today.

Latin Workbook - Level 3
Copyright © 1998 by Karen Mohs

habitō

means

**I live,
I dwell**

Write the Latin word that means **I live**.

Write the Latin word that means **now**.

nunc

means

now

fābula

means

story

Write the Latin word that means **story**.

☐ I practiced my flashcards today. (Add the new cards.)

LET'S PRACTICE

Color the box green if the Latin word matches the English meaning at the beginning of the row.

I wait for	spectō	appellō	exspectō
of the nation	populī	populōs	populus
story	fābulās	fābula	fābulae
island	īnsulam	īnsulae	īnsulās
we dwell	nārrāmus	habitō	habitāmus
province	prōvincia	prōvinciae	prōvinciās
reputations	fāma	fāmās	fāmam
of the letter	epistulās	epistula	epistulae
now	nunc	nōn	ad
of the year	annōs	annī	annus

☐ I practiced my flashcards today.

52

dēlectō

means

I please

Write the Latin word that means **I please**.

- -

_____

- -

_____

Write the Latin word that means **I labor**.

- -

_____

- -

_____

labōrō

means

**I labor, I suffer,
I am hard pressed**

causa

means

**cause,
reason**

Write the Latin word that means **cause**.

- -

_____

- -

_____

☐ I practiced my flashcards today. (Add the new cards.)

LET'S PRACTICE

Write the Latin words.

but		of the language	
villas		daughters	
now		I tell	
of the story		of the street	
tribes		we carry	
lives		with	
of the poet		of the earth	
I please		swords	
I suffer		of the queen	
of the horse		years	
gates		of the water	
causes		where?	

☐ I practiced my flashcards today.

socius

means

**comrade,
ally**

Write the Latin word that means **ally**.

_____

_____

_____

Write the Latin word that means **care**.

_____

_____

_____

dīligentia

means

**diligence,
care**

convocō

means

**I call together,
I assemble, I summon**

Write the Latin word that means **I summon**.

_____

_____

_____

☐ I practiced my flashcards today. (Add the new cards.)

LET'S PRACTICE

Match the words to their meanings.

linguae	reason	labōrō	now
vīllās	of the sailor	nunc	of the reputation
causa	of the tongue	fāmae	there are
nūntiō	farmhouses	sunt	I suffer
nautae	we summon	rēgina	of the ally
fēminam	I announce	fābulam	waters
convocāmus	we carry	socī	queen
portāmus	wife	aquās	farmer
dīligentia	even	campī	story
et	of the story	agricolam	of the plain
dēlectō	care	poēta	horses
fābulae	it is	equōs	reason
portās	I please	ad	comrades
est	luck	causam	poet
fortūna	gates	sociōs	toward

☐ I practiced my flashcards today.

LET'S PRACTICE

Write the Latin words.

comrade _____

I await _____

way _____

game _____

message _____

now _____

rumor _____

I labor _____

cause _____

I report _____

but _____

I summon _____

story _____

I name _____

envoy _____

I please _____

queen _____

with _____

I relate _____

people _____

I prepare _____

slave _____

diligence _____

I dwell _____

☐ I practiced my flashcards today.

LET'S PRACTICE

Color the light bulb yellow if the word on the bulb and on the base mean the same.

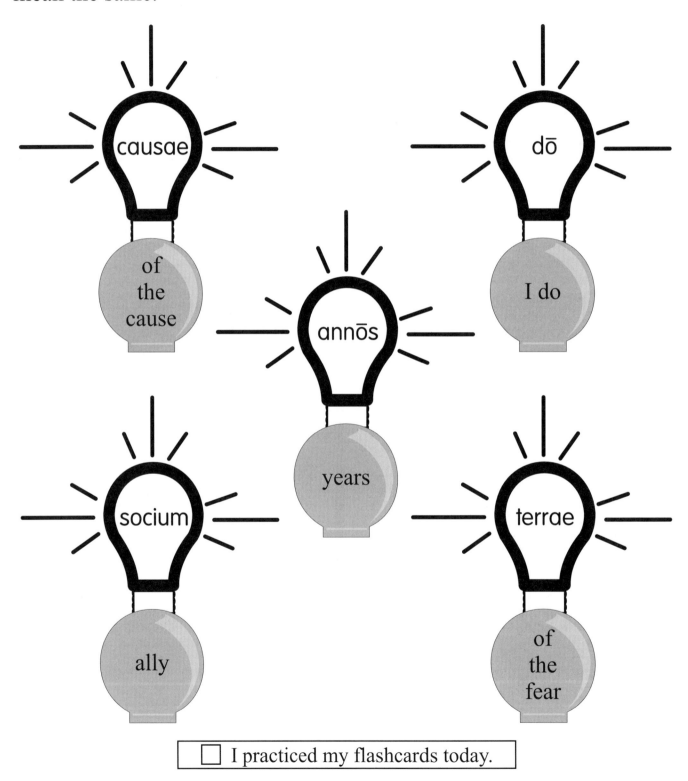

I practiced my flashcards today.

Latin Workbook - Level 3
Copyright © 1998 by Karen Mohs

LET'S PRACTICE

Write these sentences in Latin.

1. I praise the friendliness of the poet.

   __

2. We please the nations of the son.

   __

3. I tell the wife's stories.

   __

Circle the correct meanings.

populus	people	city	number
fābula	fashion	story	cable
rēgīna	queen	king	kingdom
fāma	star	hunger	report
socius	directory	comrade	party

☐ I practiced my flashcards today.

LET'S PRACTICE

Color the apple brown if the word on the apple and the word on the worm mean the same.

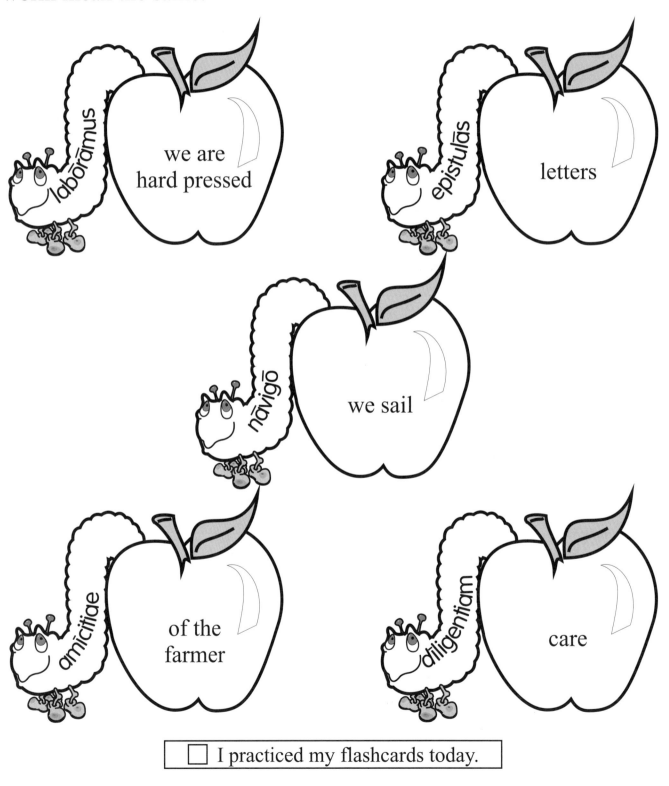

Latin Workbook - Level 3
Copyright © 1998 by Karen Mohs

LET'S PRACTICE

Match the Latin sentences to their meanings.

_____ 1. Causās nūntiāmus.   a. We seize the province.

_____ 2. Vītam amō.   b. We wait for the people.

_____ 3. Prōvinciam occupāmus.   c. I love life.

_____ 4. Fīliās spectō.   d. I look at the daughters.

_____ 5. Exspectāmus populum.   e. We report the causes.

_____ 6. Amīcī vocō fīlium.   f. I call together the poets.

_____ 7. Poētās convocō.   g. I seize the messenger.

_____ 8. Spectāmus lūdōs equī.   h. I call the friend's son.

_____ 9. Terrās pugnō rēgīnae.   i. We look at the horse's games.

_____ 10. Occupō nūntium.   j. I fight the queen's countries.

_____ 11. Sociōs fīlī pugnāmus.   k. I carry the sword.

_____ 12. Prōvinciās dō.   l. I tell the girl's stories.

_____ 13. Gladium portō.   m. We praise the friendships.

_____ 14. Laudāmus amīcitiās.   n. We fight the son's allies.

_____ 15. Fābulās puellae nārrō.   o. I grant provinces.

☐ I practiced my flashcards today.

LET'S PRACTICE

Write the meanings of these Latin sentences.

1. Īnsulam et silvam terrae appellāmus.

   It means _____

2. Fābulam nūntiō, sed fāmam nōn nūntiō.

   It means _____

3. Lēgātum et equum servī nunc laudō.

   It means _____

4. Rēgīnās exspectāmus, sed populōs nōn exspectāmus.

   It means _____

5. Viās parō et portās et vīllās.

   It means _____

Choose the correct words for the sentences. Put them in the blanks.
Then write what the sentences mean.

| patriae - patria | 1. Agricolās _____ dēlectāmus. |

   It means _____

| Tubae - Tubam | 2. _____ exspectō agricolae. |

   It means _____

| Nautās - Nauta | 3. _____ prōvinciae convocāmus. |

   It means _____

☐ I practiced my flashcards today.

Latin Workbook - Level 3
Copyright © 1998 by Karen Mohs

LET'S PRACTICE

Fill in the missing letters on the Latin words.

1. Gladi_____ port_____, et lēgāt_____ pugn_____.
   It means **I carry the sword, and I fight the lieutenant.**

2. Nāvig_____, et spectāmus īnsul_____ rēgīnae.
   It means **We sail, and we look at the queen's islands.**

3. Patri_____ naut_____ am_____.
   It means **We love the native land of the sailor.**

Match the words to their meanings.

nūntius	reason	epistula	slaves
annōs	I live	servōs	letter
amīcum	news	nāvigō	chance
causa	years	lūdus	care
habitō	friend	fortūnam	school
fāmās	life	dīligentia	I sail
vītam	reputations	nātūrās	natures

☐ I practiced my flashcards today.

LET'S PRACTICE

Draw a line from each noodle to the correct soup kettle.

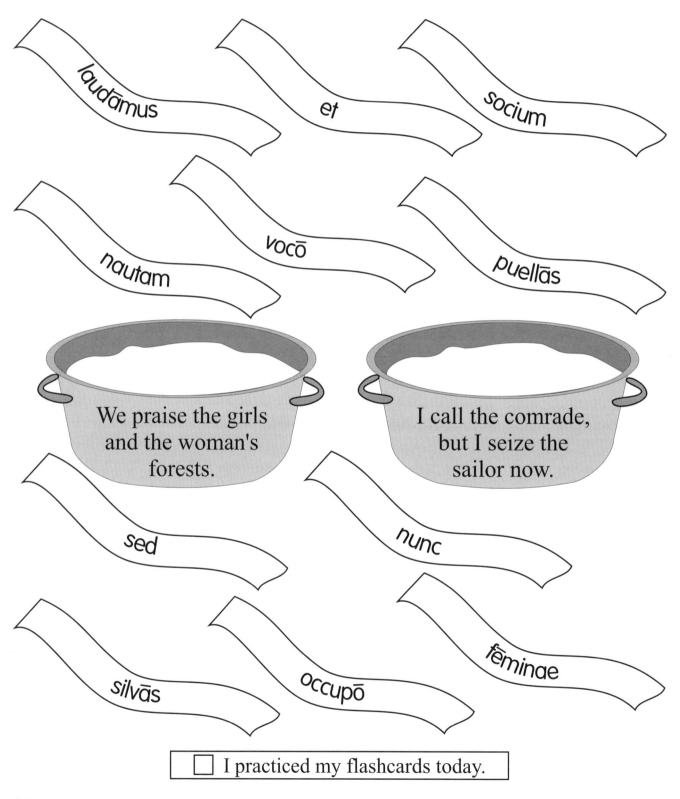

laudāmus

et

socium

nautam

vocō

puellās

We praise the girls
and the woman's
forests.

I call the comrade,
but I seize the
sailor now.

sed

nunc

silvās

occupō

fēmina

☐ I practiced my flashcards today.

LET'S PRACTICE

Fill in the blanks with the correct words from the boxes on the right.
Then write the meanings of the sentences.

1. Servum _____ vocāmus.

   It means _____

socius
lēgātī
exspectō

2. Poētam et fēminam _____.

   It means _____

appellō
lūdus
via

3. Tubās et _____ parāmus.

   It means _____

sed
labōrō
gladiōs

4. _____ nunc rēgīnam populī.

   It means _____

Cum
Nōn
Amō

5. Aquās _____ nōn occupāmus.

   It means _____

nūntiō
īnsulae
populus

6. Dēlectō filiās et _____.

   It means _____

fēminās
parō
fābula

7. _____ poētae spectō.

   It means _____

Dīligentia
Epistulās
Habitō

☐ I practiced my flashcards today.

LET'S PRACTICE

Draw pictures for these sentences.

Causās nārrāmus, sed gladiōs socī nōn portāmus.

Causās nārrō, sed gladium socī nōn portō.

I practiced my flashcards today.

Vīllam puellae amō.

It means **I like the farmhouse** *of the girl.*

or

I like the *girl's* **farmhouse.**

Vīllam puellārum amō.

It means **I like the farmhouse** *of the girls.*

or

I like the *girls'* **farmhouse.**

The new ending is ārum. Just as ae at the end of words like puella shows that the farmhouse belongs to the girl, ārum shows it belongs to more than one girl.

Vīllam filiōrum* amō.

It means **I like the farmhouse** *of the sons.*

or

I like the *sons'* **farmhouse.**

Vīllam amīcōrum amō.

It means **I like the farmhouse** *of the friends.*

or

I like the *friends'* **farmhouse.**

The new ending is ōrum. It replaces the us at the end of words like filius or amīcus to show that the farmhouse belongs to more than one son (or more than one friend).

Circle the words that mean belonging to more than one son or friend.

filiōrum   filōrum   amīciōrum   amīcōrum

*Careful. Don't forget to keep the i if the word normally ends in ius. Notice the difference. As we learned on page 39, *singular* words, when used to show possession, do *not* keep the i before the ī ending (e.g. filī).

☐ I practiced my flashcards today. (Add the new cards.)

LET'S PRACTICE

Fill in the blanks with the correct Latin words.

1. Epistulam _____ exspectō.
(of the farmer)

2. Patriam pugnāmus _____.
(of the lieutenants)

3. Memoriās _____ nūntiō.
(of the daughters)

4. Amīcōs _____ laudāmus.
(of the poets)

Match the Latin words to their meanings.

____ 1. patriārum   a. of the horse

____ 2. nautae   b. of the native lands

____ 3. patriae   c. of the native land

____ 4. equōrum   d. of the sailors

____ 5. equī   e. of the messengers

____ 6. nautārum   f. of the sailor

____ 7. nūntiōrum   g. of the horses

☐ I practiced my flashcards today.

68

LET'S PRACTICE

Write the Latin words.

of the wives ⸺⸺⸺⸺⸺	of the sword ⸺⸺⸺⸺⸺
of the water ⸺⸺⸺⸺⸺	of the years ⸺⸺⸺⸺⸺
of the life ⸺⸺⸺⸺⸺	of the sons ⸺⸺⸺⸺⸺
of the forests ⸺⸺⸺⸺⸺	of the friend ⸺⸺⸺⸺⸺
of the message ⸺⸺⸺⸺⸺	of the allies ⸺⸺⸺⸺⸺
of the schools ⸺⸺⸺⸺⸺	of the way ⸺⸺⸺⸺⸺

Circle **yes** or **no**.

yes   no   1. Latin puellārum means **of the girls**.

yes   no   2. Latin fīliae means **of the daughters**.

yes   no   3. Latin gladiōrum means **of the sword**.

yes   no   4. Latin lūdī means **of the school**.

yes   no   5. Latin silvae means **of the forests**.

yes   no   6. Latin amīcōrum means **of the friends**.

yes   no   7. Latin fābulae means **of the story**.

yes   no   8. Latin vīllārum means **of the country house**.

☐ I practiced my flashcards today.

LET'S PRACTICE

Circle the correct Latin words. Then write what the sentences mean.

1. Prōvinciam et campōs agricolārum / agricola occupāmus.

   It means _____

2. Portō memoriam puellae. / puella.

   It means _____

3. Linguam / Lingua et lūdum populōrum / populus appellō.

   It means _____

4. Filiōs / Filius et equōs filiōrum convocāmus.

   It means _____

5. Diligentia / Diligentiam servōrum nōn pugnāmus.

   It means _____

6. Aqua / Aquam spectō, et nātūram amō.

   It means _____

7. Litterās filī / filius et nūntiōs terra / terrārum exspectāmus.

   It means _____

8. Laudō amīcitiam rēgīnārum / rēgīna, sed rēgīnās nōn laudō.

   It means _____

9. Vīllam / Vīlla parāmus, et filia / filiam vocāmus.

   It means _____

☐ I practiced my flashcards today.

Puellam amō. It means **I like the girl.**

Puellam amat. It means *He* (*she* or *it*) **likes the girl.**

Puellam portō. It means **I carry the girl.**

Puellam portat. It means *He* (*she* or *it*) **carries the girl.**

Fill in the blank with ō or āmus or at.

If I want to say *I* do something, I use the ending _____.

If I want to say *we* do something, I use the ending _____.

If I want to say *he* does something, I use the ending _____.

Match the Latin words to their meanings.

_____ 1. nāvigāmus   a. she sails

_____ 2. labōrō   b. I sail

_____ 3. dat   c. I am hard pressed

_____ 4. nāvigat   d. he is hard pressed

_____ 5. labōrāmus   e. we sail

_____ 6. nāvigō   f. we are hard pressed

_____ 7. labōrat   g. it gives

☐ I practiced my flashcards today. (Add the new cards.)

LET'S PRACTICE

Draw lines from the Latin sentences to their meanings.

Lēgātōs prōvinciārum vocō.

We call the provinces' envoys.

Lēgātōs prōvinciārum vocāmus.

I call the provinces' envoys.

Lēgātōs prōvinciārum vocat.

He calls the provinces' envoys.

Equōs agricolārum exspectat.

She awaits the farmers' horses.

Equōs agricolārum exspectō.

We await the farmers' horses.

Equōs agricolārum exspectāmus.

I await the farmers' horses.

Nārrō dīligentiās puellae.

We relate the girl's cares.

Nārrat dīligentiās puellae.

I relate the girl's cares.

Nārrāmus dīligentiās puellae.

She relates the girl's cares.

Portam vīllae spectat.

I look at the villa's gate.

Portam vīllae spectāmus.

We look at the villa's gate.

Portam vīllae spectō.

He looks at the villa's gate.

Fēminās īnsulārum dēlectāmus.

It pleases the islands' wives.

Fēminās īnsulārum dēlectō.

We please the islands' wives.

Fēminās īnsulārum dēlectat.

I please the islands' wives.

☐ I practiced my flashcards today.

LET'S PRACTICE

Write the meanings on the lines below the Latin sentences.

Nautās pugnat.	Gladiōs portāmus.
_____	_____
Nautam pugnō.	Gladium portat.
_____	_____
Nūntium parat.	Fābulās nūntiat.
_____	_____
Nūntiōs parāmus.	Fābulam nūntiāmus.
_____	_____
Populōs convocat.	Sociōs appellāmus.
_____	_____
Populum convocō.	Socium appellat.
_____	_____

Choose the correct words for the sentences. Put them in the blanks.
Then write what the sentences mean.

_____
- - - - - - - - - - - - - - -

| sed - laudat | 1. Viam et campum _____. |

It means _____

_____
- - - - - - - - - - - - - - -

| amat - nunc | 2. Puellam nōn _____. |

It means _____

☐ I practiced my flashcards today.

LET'S PRACTICE

Color the muffin brown if the words inside mean the same.

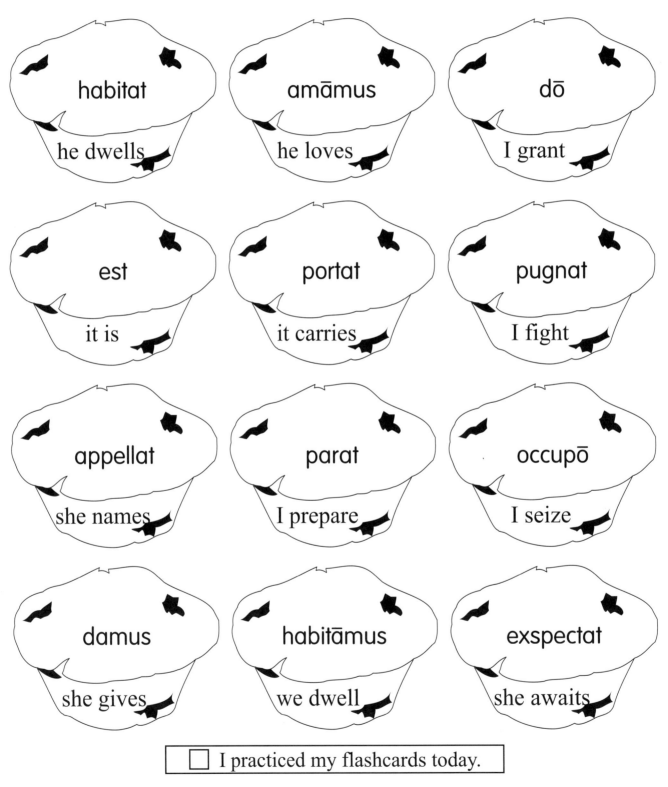

| habitat | amāmus | dō |
| he dwells | he loves | I grant |

| est | portat | pugnat |
| it is | it carries | I fight |

| appellat | parat | occupō |
| she names | I prepare | I seize |

| damus | habitāmus | exspectat |
| she gives | we dwell | she awaits |

☐ I practiced my flashcards today.

74

Latin Workbook - Level 3
Copyright © 1998 by Karen Mohs

Puellam amat.

It means **He likes the girl.**

Now let's use a word that tells us who *he* is.

Let's use *the farmer*.

Agricola puellam amat.

It means **The farmer likes the girl.**

Fill in the blanks with the correct words from the boxes on the right.
Then write the meanings of the sentences.

1. _____ gladium spectat.

   It means _____

   | Lēgātōs |
   | Lēgātus |
   | Lēgātum |

2. _____ fābulās nārrat.

   It means _____

   | Poēta |
   | Poētam |
   | Poētās |

3. _____ amīcōs convocat.

   It means _____

   | Fīliās |
   | Fīlia |
   | Fīliam |

4. _____ īnsulam occupat.

   It means _____

   | Fīliōs |
   | Fīlium |
   | Fīlius |

☐ I practiced my flashcards today.

LET'S PRACTICE

Fill in the blanks with the correct Latin words.

_____

1. _____ viās, sed nōn parō equōs.
   (I prepare)

2. Fīliōs et fīliās _____ exspectāmus.
   (of the queen)

3. _____ fāmam poētārum nōn nūntiat.
   (the farmer)

4. Portās et viās vīllārum nunc _____.
   (we look at)

5. _____ fīlium lēgātī et fēminae portat.
   (the girl)

6. _____ lēgātum dēlectat, sed rēgīnam nōn dēlectat.
   (the slave)

7. _____ et sociōs fēminārum laudō.
   (the friends)

8. Amīcus socium et equum _____ vocat.
   (of the farmer)

☐ I practiced my flashcards today.

Latin Workbook - Level 3
Copyright © 1998 by Karen Mohs

LET'S PRACTICE

Write the meanings of these Latin sentences.

1. Fīlius fīliam amat, et fīlia fīlium.*

   It means _____

2. Aquam spectō, sed nautās nōn vocō.

   It means _____

3. Nautae fēmina equōs lēgātī parat.

   It means _____

4. Fābulās poētārum et rēgīnārum nunc nārrāmus.

   It means _____

5. Lēgātus gladium dat, sed causam nōn dat.

   It means _____

6. Amīcus fīliārum nāvigat, et epistulās exspectat.

   It means _____

7. Gladiōs socī occupō, et populōs pugnō.

   It means _____

8. Nūntiōs convocāmus, et fāmās laudāmus.

   It means _____

9. Agricola fēminam et poētam et servum vocat.

   It means _____

*It appears that this second clause is without a verb. However, the verb amat, which is seen in the first clause, is understood to be the verb of the second clause as well.

☐ I practiced my flashcards today.

LET'S PRACTICE

Circle the correct Latin words.

of fortunes	he dwells	of the school
fortūnās fortūnārum fortūnae	habitat habitāmus habitō	lūdōrum lūdōs lūdī
native lands	of the lives	we please
patriās patria patriārum	vītās vītārum vītae	dēlectāmus dēlectat dēlectō
of the lands	I sail	care
terrae terrārum terrās	nāvigāmus nāvigat nāvigō	dīligentiae dīligentiās dīligentiam
friendliness	of the tongues	natures
amīcitiam amīcitiās amīcitiārum	linguae linguārum lingua	nātūrārum nātūram nātūrās
of the year	I dwell	of the memories
annōrum annī annus	habitat habitāmus habitō	memoriārum memoriam memoriās

☐ I practiced my flashcards today.

Puellam amō.   It means **I like the girl.**

Puellam amāmus.   It means **We like the girl.**

Puellam amat.   It means **He (she, it) likes the girl.**

Puellam amant.   It means *They* **like the girl.**

Fill in the blank with ō or āmus or at or ant.

If I want to say *he* does something, I use the ending _____.

If I want to say *I* do something, I use the ending _____.

If I want to say *they* do something, I use the ending _____.

If I want to say *we* do something, I use the ending _____.

Write the meanings on the lines below the Latin sentences.

Amīcōs exspectat.	Tubam spectō.
_____	_____
Amīcum exspectant.	Tubās spectant.
_____	_____
Rēgīnās laudant.	Īnsulam occupāmus.
_____	_____
Rēginam laudāmus.	Īnsulās occupat.
_____	_____

☐ I practiced my flashcards today. (Add the new cards.)

LET'S PRACTICE

Match the words to their meanings.

amant	she loves	parat	it prepares
amat	they love	parant	they prepare
amāmus	we love	parō	I prepare
occupat	they seize	labōrāmus	they labor
occupant	I seize	labōrant	we labor
occupō	it seizes	labōrat	he labors
nārrat	they tell	nūntiant	I report
nārrāmus	we tell	nūntiāmus	they report
nārrant	he tells	nūntiō	we report
dēlectō	it pleases	portāmus	she carries
dēlectant	I please	portat	they carry
dēlectat	they please	portant	we carry
pugnāmus	we fight	nāvigō	we sail
pugnat	they fight	nāvigant	they sail
pugnant	he fights	nāvigāmus	I sail

☐ I practiced my flashcards today.

LET'S PRACTICE

Write the sentences using the words on the right.

1. _____

   It means **They summon the sons.**

convocant
epistulam
fīliōs
fīlius
nāvigat
portō

2. _____

   It means **The son sails.**

3. _____

   It means **I carry the letter.**

4. _____

   It means **We look at the plains.**

campōs
poētam
poētās
spectāmus
spectō
vocant

5. _____

   It means **They call the poets.**

6. _____

   It means **I look at the poet.**

☐ I practiced my flashcards today.

LET'S PRACTICE

Connect each orange to the correct basket.

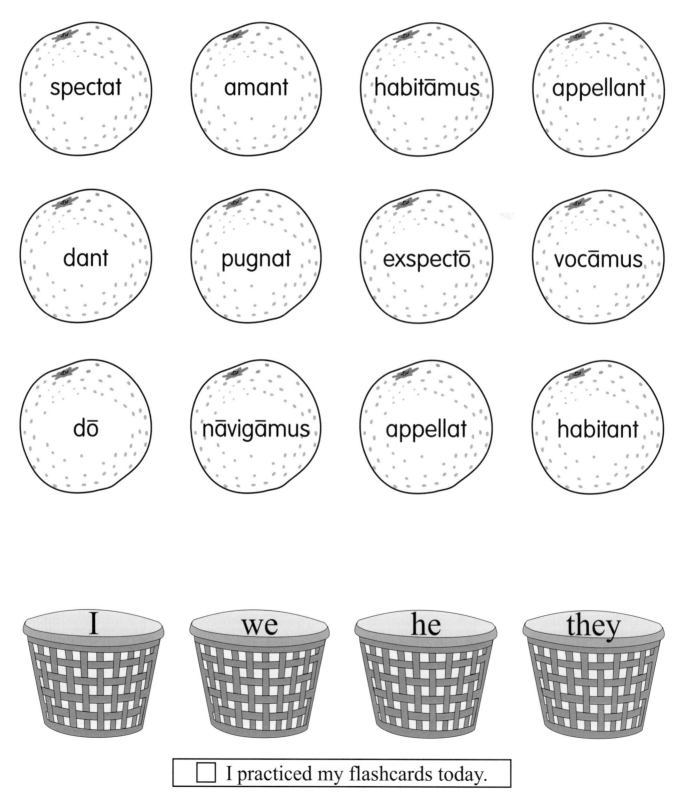

spectat amant habitāmus appellant

dant pugnat exspectō vocāmus

dō nāvigāmus appellat habitant

I we he they

☐ I practiced my flashcards today.

Latin Workbook - Level 3
Copyright © 1998 by Karen Mohs

Now for more than one!

puella	It means **the girl.**
puellae*	It means **the _girls_.**
fēmina	It means **the woman.**
fēminae	It means **the _women_.**

fīlius	It means **the son.**
fīliī**	It means **the _sons_.**
equus	It means **the horse.**
equī	It means **the _horses_.**

It's your turn!

Fill in the blank with a or ae or ī or us.

Port_____ means **the gate**.   Gladi_____ means **the sword**.

Port_____ means **the gates**.   Gladi_____ means **the swords**.

*Sometimes endings for different uses have the same spelling. For example, puellae, as taught here, means more than one girl. However, as we have learned earlier, it can also mean that something belongs to the girl. (See page 39.)

**Notice that the words ending in ius retain the i of the base when meaning more than one, as in fīliī. It will be remembered that, in singular words, the i was dropped when showing possession (i.e., when showing that something belongs to something, as in fīlī.) (See page 39.)

☐ I practiced my flashcards today. (Add the new cards.)

LET'S PRACTICE

Color the box orange if the English meaning matches the Latin word at the beginning of the row.

puellae	of the girls	girls	girl
campum	of the plain	plains	plain
amīcī	friends	friend	of the friends
vītās	life	of the lives	lives
poētae	of the poets	poet	poets
tubārum	trumpets	of the trumpets	of the trumpet
patriae	of the country	of the countries	country
viae	street	streets	of the streets
populī	tribes	of the tribes	tribe
fīlī	son	sons	of the son

☐ I practiced my flashcards today.

LET'S PRACTICE

Match the words to their meanings.

puella		puellae		
	girl			of the girls
puellae		puellārum		
	of the girl			girls
puellam		puellās		

---

annum		annī		
	of the year			years
annus		annōrum		
	year			of the years
annī		annōs		

Put a check in the box when you notice:

☐ **Puella** and **puellam** both mean **girl**. The ending **a** is used to tell who is doing* the action. The ending **am** is used to tell who is receiving** the action.

☐ **Annus** and **annum** both mean **year**. The ending **us** is used to tell who is doing the action. The ending **um** is used to tell who is receiving the action.

☐ **Puellae** and **puellās** both mean **girls**. The ending **ae** is used to tell who is doing the action. The ending **ās** is used to tell who is receiving the action.

☐ **Annī** and **annōs** both mean **years**. The ending **ī** is used to tell who is doing the action. The ending **ōs** is used to tell who is receiving the action.

*This is the subject of the sentence.
**This is the object of the sentence.

☐ I practiced my flashcards today.

Puellam amant.

It means **They like the girl.**

Now let's use a word that tells us who *they* are.
Let's use *the farmers*.

Agricolae puellam amant.

It means **The farmers like the girl.**

Match the Latin sentences to their meanings.

_____ 1. Fīliī laudant.   a. They praise the sons.

_____ 2. Fīliōs laudant.   b. The sons praise.

_____ 3. Fīliae dēlectant.   c. The daughters please.

_____ 4. Fīliās dēlectant.   d. They please the daughters.

_____ 5. Fēminae convocant.   e. The wives summon.

_____ 6. Fēminās convocant.   f. They summon the wives.

_____ 7. Nūntiī pugnant.   g. They fight the messengers.

_____ 8. Nūntiōs pugnant.   h. The messengers fight.

☐ I practiced my flashcards today.

Latin Workbook - Level 3
Copyright © 1998 by Karen Mohs

LET'S PRACTICE

Choose the best words for the sentences below. Then write what the sentences mean.

poēta	litterās	sociōrum

1. _____ et tubās portant.

   It means _____

2. Agricolae fāmās _____ exspectant.

   It means _____

3. _____ fīliās fēminārum nōn dēlectat.

   It means _____

servōrum	servī	servōs

1. Puella _____ populōrum convocat.

   It means _____

2. _____ appellant viās patriārum.

   It means _____

3. Nautae equōs _____ vocant.

   It means _____

☐ I practiced my flashcards today.

LET'S PRACTICE

Connect each lightning bolt to the correct cloud.

We prepare the gates and the schools of the queen.

The queen prepares the gate of the school.

rēginae

parāmus

et

lūdī

lūdōs

portās

portam

rēgina

parat

☐ I practiced my flashcards today.

LET'S PRACTICE

Fill in the blanks with the correct Latin words. Then write what the sentences mean.

1. Lēgātī aquās īnsulae _____.
   _____ (look at)

   It means _____

2. Pugnāmus populum _____ agricolae.
   _____ (of the friend)

   It means _____

3. _____ fābulam nautārum nūntiant.
   (the comrades)

   It means _____

4. Rēgīnae parant terram, sed nōn _____.
   _____ (suffer)

   It means _____

5. Silvās et īnsulās _____ laudō.
   _____ (of the earth)

   It means _____

☐ I practiced my flashcards today.

PUZZLE TIME

Think of the meanings of the English words. Then write the Latin words on the puzzle below.

across	down
1. I await	2. but
3. I announce	3. I tell
7. boy	4. news
8. play	5. earth
10. now	6. memory
12. I assemble	8. envoy
13. rumor	9. comrade
14. reason	11. story
16. slave	14. with
17. near	15. I like
18. I give	
19. queen	

☐ I practiced my flashcards today.

Latin Workbook - Level 3
Copyright © 1998 by Karen Mohs

LET'S PRACTICE

Draw lines to connect the parts of the sentences.

1. Sociī equum rēgīnae   patriam nūntī.

2. Puella lēgātōs et agricolās   laudant.

3. Nunc nōn amō   convocat.

Now write the sentences you have made. First write them in Latin.
Then write what they mean.

1. _____

   It means _____

2. _____

   It means _____

3. _____

   It means _____

CHALLENGE!
Can you write this sentence in Latin?

     The son of the woman carries the sword of the sailor.

_____

_____

☐ I practiced my flashcards today.

LET'S PRACTICE

Draw pictures for these sentences.

Fēminae agricolās exspectant, sed agricolae fēminās nōn exspectant.

Īnsulam nunc occupāmus, et litterās portāmus.

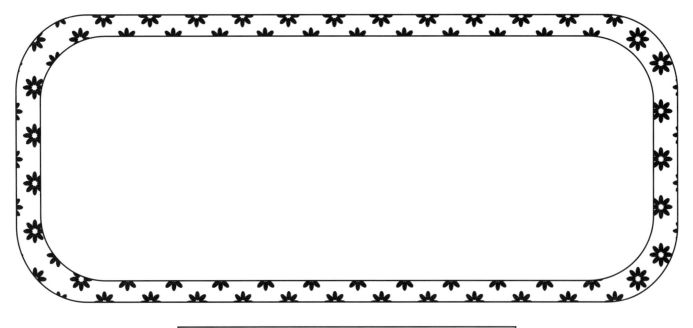

☐ I practiced my flashcards today.

superō

means

**I surpass,
I defeat**

Write the Latin word that means **I defeat**.

_____
- - - - - - - - - - - - - - - - -
_____
- - - - - - - - - - - - - - - - -
_____
- - - - - - - - - - - - - - - - -

Write the Latin word that means **plenty**.

_____
- - - - - - - - - - - - - - - - -
_____
- - - - - - - - - - - - - - - - -
_____
- - - - - - - - - - - - - - - - -

cōpia

means

**plenty,
supply**

in

means

**into, against,
in, on**

Write the Latin word that means **in**.

_____
- - - - - - - - - - - - - - - - -
_____
- - - - - - - - - - - - - - - - -
_____
- - - - - - - - - - - - - - - - -

☐ I practiced my flashcards today. (Add the new cards.)

LET'S PRACTICE

Circle the correct Latin words.

on	I defeat	we are hard pressed
ad cum in	superat superō superāmus	labōrāmus labōrat labōrant
lives	I call	they grant
vītārum vītās vīta	vocō vocāmus vocant	dat dō dant
reason	we dwell	of care
causae causārum causam	habitō habitat habitāmus	dīligentiae dīligentia dīligentiam
she tells	plenty	friendships
nārrant nārrāmus nārrat	cōpia cōpiae cōpiārum	amīcitiae amīcitia amīcitiārum
he sails	of fortunes	they prepare
nāvigat nāvigāmus nāvigant	fortūnās fortūnārum fortūnam	parāmus parat parant

☐ I practiced my flashcards today.

oppugnō

means

I attack

Write the Latin word that means **I attack**.

_____

_____

_____

Write the Latin word that means **long**.

_____

_____

_____

diū

means

for a long time, long

vulnerō

means

I wound

Write the Latin word that means **I wound**.

_____

_____

_____

☐ I practiced my flashcards today. (Add the new cards.)

LET'S PRACTICE

Write the meanings of these Latin words.

agricolās _____

vocāmus _____

laudant _____

nāvigō _____

servus _____

nātūra _____

fīliam _____

diū _____

fīliī _____

porta _____

īnsulās _____

vulnerat _____

annōrum _____

silvam _____

fīlī _____

portant _____

vīta _____

annōs _____

fābulās _____

gladī _____

annum _____

sociī _____

poēta _____

oppugnō _____

dēlectat _____

amīcum _____

vītārum _____

pugnant _____

rēgīna _____

vocō _____

☐ I practiced my flashcards today.

Latin Workbook - Level 3
Copyright © 1998 by Karen Mohs

fuga

means

**flight,
exile**

Write the Latin word that means **flight**.

_____

_____

_____

Write the Latin word that means **already**.

_____

_____

iam

means

**now,
already**

Write the Latin word that means **I try**.

temptō

means

**I try,
I attempt**

_____

_____

_____

☐ I practiced my flashcards today. (Add the new cards.)

LET'S PRACTICE

Match the words to their meanings.

amīcitiam	exile		dīligentia	care
lingua	friendliness		superat	of the daughters
laudāmus	we praise		filiārum	reputation
fuga	tongue		habitō	it defeats
filiōrum	plains		fāmam	I dwell
temptō	of the sons		iam	flights
campī	I attempt		fugās	already
vulnerat	he wounds		oppugnant	of the water
amat	I capture		damus	we attempt
cōpiae	of supply		temptāmus	we give
occupō	she likes		aquae	they attack
convocant	of supplies		viae	streets
annum	they summon		lūdus	forests
diū	year		lēgātōrum	play
cōpiārum	long		silvās	of the envoys

☐ I practiced my flashcards today.

herī

means

yesterday

Write the Latin word that means **yesterday**.

- -

_____

- -

_____

Write the Latin word that means **I keep**.

- -

_____

- -

_____

servō

means

I guard, I save, I keep

poena

means

penalty, punishment

Write the Latin word that means **penalty**.

- -

_____

- -

_____

☐ I practiced my flashcards today. (Add the new cards.)

LET'S PRACTICE

Color the box red if the English meaning matches the Latin word at the beginning of the row.

amīcī	of the friends	of the friend	friend
herī	today	tomorrow	yesterday
vulnerant	we wound	they wound	it wounds
fugae	flights	of the flights	flight
servat	they guard	she guards	I guard
iam	already	where	today
cōpiam	supply	of the supplies	supplies
causās	cause	causes	of the causes
poena	of the penalty	penalties	penalty
epistula	letter	of the letter	of the letters

☐ I practiced my flashcards today.

semper

means

always

Write the Latin word that means **always**.

_____

Write the Latin word that means **captive**.

captīvus

means

captive

locus

means

place, location, situation

Write the Latin word that means **place**.

_____

☐ I practiced my flashcards today. (Add the new cards.)

LET'S PRACTICE

Choose the correct words for the sentences. Put them in the blanks.
Then write what the sentences mean.

Fīliī - Fīlī

1. _____ superant agricolās rēgīnae.

It means _____

nūntiī - nūntiōs

2. Semper oppugnō _____.

It means _____

spectant - spectat

3. Captīvī _____ servum.

It means _____

Poenae - Poenam

4. _____ populī nūntiāmus.

It means _____

vulnerat - vulnerant

5. Equus puellās _____.

It means _____

īnsula - īnsulae

6. Portam _____ servāmus.

It means _____

oppugnō - oppugnat

7. Populus nōn _____.

It means _____

☐ I practiced my flashcards today.

Latin Workbook - Level 3
Copyright © 1998 by Karen Mohs

audācia

means

boldness, daring

Write the Latin word that means **daring**.

_____

- - - - - - - - - - - - - - - - - -

_____

- - - - - - - - - - - - - - - - - -

_____

Write the Latin word that means **today**.

_____

- - - - - - - - - - - - - - - - - -

_____

- - - - - - - - - - - - - - - - - -

_____

hodiē

means

today

volō

means

I fly

Write the Latin word that means **I fly**.

_____

- - - - - - - - - - - - - - - - - -

_____

- - - - - - - - - - - - - - - - - -

_____

☐ I practiced my flashcards today. (Add the new cards.)

LET'S PRACTICE

Write the Latin words.

they announce _____

of the penalty _____

she prepares _____

I fly _____

we give _____

already _____

we save _____

of the flight _____

he fights _____

I name _____

always _____

they sail _____

it tries _____

I dwell _____

yesterday _____

of the native lands _____

we surpass _____

they attempt _____

he likes _____

I attack _____

today _____

they wound _____

of the year _____

of the poet _____

☐ I practiced my flashcards today.

Latin Workbook - Level 3
Copyright © 1998 by Karen Mohs

animus

means

mind, spirit

Write the Latin word that means **mind**.

_____

_____

_____

Write the Latin word that means **tomorrow**.

_____

_____

_____

crās

means

tomorrow

carrus

means

cart, wagon

Write the Latin word that means **cart**.

_____

_____

_____

☐ I practiced my flashcards today. (Add the new cards.)

LET'S PRACTICE

Color the box purple if the Latin word matches the English meaning at the beginning of the row.

punishment	poenās	poena	poenārum
daring	audāciae	audāciam	audāciās
of the captive	captīvī	captīvōrum	captīvōs
tomorrow	herī	hodiē	crās
exiles	fuga	fugam	fugās
wagon	carrī	carrus	carrōrum
situations	locus	locī	locōrum
of the daughters	filiārum	filiās	filia
care	dīligentiās	dīligentiae	dīligentia
mind	animus	animōs	animōrum

☐ I practiced my flashcards today.

LET'S PRACTICE

Write the meanings of these Latin words.

dēlectō _____

servōrum _____

temptō _____

carrōs _____

volāmus _____

epistula _____

semper _____

cōpia _____

vīta _____

captīvōs _____

nāvigat _____

lūdum _____

lingua _____

oppugnant _____

gladiī _____

diū _____

sociī _____

occupat _____

audācia _____

iam _____

animum _____

filiōrum _____

porta _____

servāmus _____

lēgātus _____

nārrant _____

nātūra _____

causās _____

via _____

vulnerō _____

☐ I practiced my flashcards today.

LET'S PRACTICE

Color the hat yellow if the words mean the same.

they love
amant

penalties
poenās

he keeps
servō

yesterday
herī

I defeat
superant

of the
ally
socī

place
locum

they fly
volō

flights
fugae

she carries
portāmus

friends
audāciās

I call
vocō

of the
wagons
carrum

today
hodiē

I report
nūntiō

plenty
cōpiam

☐ I practiced my flashcards today.

LET'S PRACTICE

Match the words to their meanings.

servat	now	amat	minds
dīligentiās	it attacks	populum	he likes
oppugnat	she guards	nauta	people
iam	cares	animōs	sailor
semper	always	fuga	they wound
crās	of schools	vulnerant	they assemble
audāciae	tomorrow	convocant	flight
lūdōrum	punishment	volant	for a long time
poenam	of daring	diū	they fly
animōrum	captives	locus	I wait for
captīvōs	we please	exspectō	situation
dēlectāmus	of the spirits	oppugnō	I attack
laudāmus	we praise	superō	of the wagon
nūntī	of the life	carrī	I surpass
vītae	of the news	tuba	trumpet

☐ I practiced my flashcards today.

Latin Workbook - Level 3
Copyright © 1998 by Karen Mohs

LET'S PRACTICE

Shoot the arrows to their targets.

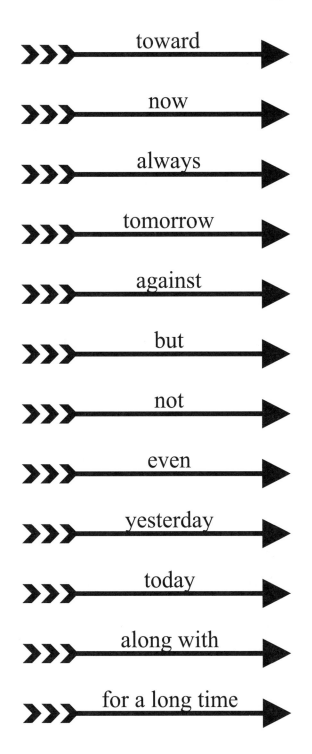

toward

now

always

tomorrow

against

but

not

even

yesterday

today

along with

for a long time

sed
semper

ad
in

crās
iam

et
herī

nōn
cum

diū
hodiē

☐ I practiced my flashcards today.

LET'S PRACTICE

Put the endings in the boxes on the Latin words in the sentences.

am	at
ae	a

1. Puell_ fēmin___ naut__ port_.

   It means **The girl carries the sailor's wife.**

ōrum	ās
āmus	ōs

2. Anim__ soci____ nunc laud____.

   It means **Now we praise the minds of the allies.**

ant	ae
ās	ōrum

3. Poēt__ memori__ popul____ serv__.

   It means **The poets keep the nations' memories.**

at	ō
ō	um

4. Gladi___ port_, sed nōn pugn_.

   It means **I carry the sword, but I do not fight.**

at	ōs
ae	at

5. Vulner_ et super_ lēgāt__ rēgin__.

   It means **He wounds and defeats the queen's envoys.**

at	us
ōs	ae

6. Captīv__ carr__ īnsul__ laud__.

   It means **The captive praises the island's carts.**

☐ I practiced my flashcards today.

LET'S PRACTICE

Connect each bowling pin to the correct bowling ball.

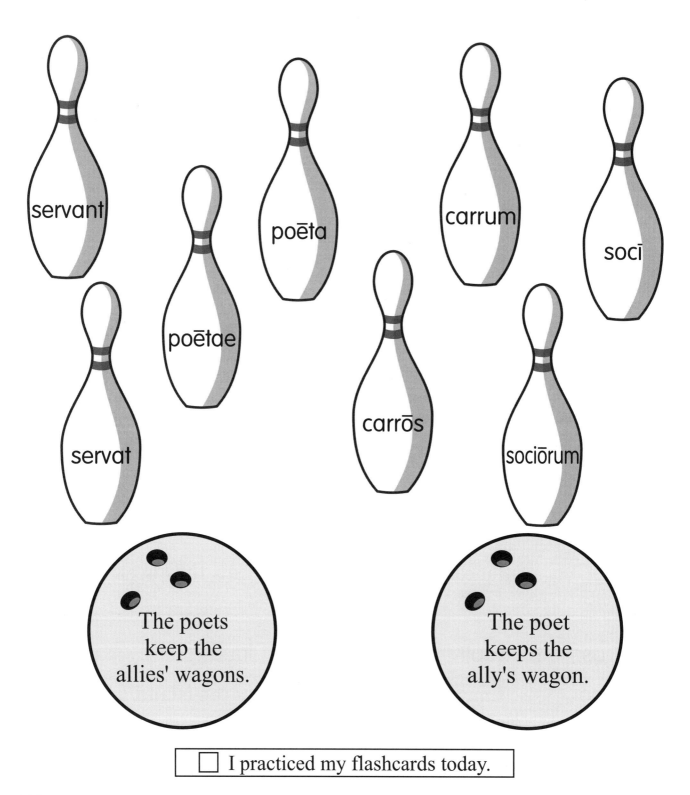

Latin Workbook - Level 3
Copyright © 1998 by Karen Mohs

LET'S PRACTICE

Circle the correct Latin words. Then write what the sentences mean.

1. Nūntius hodiē portat / portant cōpiās amīcōrum.

   It means _____

2. Dīligentiam filiārum rēgīna nunc exspectāmus. / exspectat.

   It means _____

3. Fīliōs lēgātī vocāmus, sed nōn fīlia. / fīliās.

   It means _____

4. Prōvinciās / Prōvinciae oppugnō, sed populōs nōn superō.

   It means _____

5. Sociī equōs et gladius / gladiōs iam parant.

   It means _____

6. Puella vīllam et silvam et īnsulam dant. / dat.

   It means _____

7. Poenās nūntiāmus nautārum / nauta et agricolārum.

   It means _____

8. Fēmina filiam et filium amīcī convocāmus. / convocat.

   It means _____

9. Fīlius / Fīliī locōs et portās lūdōrum spectant.

   It means _____

☐ I practiced my flashcards today.

LET'S PRACTICE

Draw pictures for these sentences.

Equī hodiē volant, sed tubae et carrī nōn volant.

Nauta fābulās īnsulae et patriae diū nārrat.

☐ I practiced my flashcards today.

LET'S PRACTICE

Fill in the blanks with the correct words from the boxes on the right. Then write the meanings of the sentences.

1. Nautae _____ vulnerant.

   It means _____

   | puella |
   | agricola |
   | agricolās |

2. Poētam laudāmus _____.

   It means _____

   | pugnō |
   | populī |
   | nūntiī |

3. _____, et rēgīnam dēlectat.

   It means _____

   | Habitat |
   | Campōrum |
   | Fīliī |

4. Epistulās fīlī diū _____.

   It means _____

   | crās |
   | herī |
   | spectō |

5. _____ fugae nunc nārrāmus.

   It means _____

   | Causās |
   | Fābula |
   | Habitō |

6. Amīcōs _____ semper vocant.

   It means _____

   | fēminōs |
   | fēminārum |
   | fēmina |

7. Fāmās prōvinciārum hodiē _____.

   It means _____

   | audāciae |
   | cum |
   | damus |

☐ I practiced my flashcards today.

Latin Workbook - Level 3
Copyright © 1998 by Karen Mohs

PUZZLE TIME

Think of the meanings of the English words. Then write the Latin words on the puzzle below.

across		down	
1. boldness		1. mind	17. I grant
8. penalty		2. wagon	18. with
9. yesterday		3. toward	20. and
10. story		4. way	
12. where?		5. situation	
13. captive		6. already	
16. always		7. flight	
17. I please		9. today	
19. I guard		11. I try	
21. I fly		13. tomorrow	
22. rumor		14. boy	
		15. I like	

☐ I practiced my flashcards today.

116

Amō puellam.   It means **I like the girl.**

Amās puellam.   It means **You like the girl.**

(The ending **ās** means only one **you**. When there are several of **you**, a different word is used. We will learn it later.)

Portō gladium.   It means **I carry the sword.**

Portās gladium.   It means **You carry the sword.**

Match the Latin words to their meanings.

exspectāmus	I await
exspectō	you await
exspectat	we await
exspectās	they await
exspectant	he awaits
superās	we surpass
superat	they surpass
superāmus	you surpass
superant	I surpass
superō	he surpasses

☐ I practiced my flashcards today. (Add the new cards.)

LET'S PRACTICE

Fill in the blanks with the correct Latin words. Then write what the sentences mean.

1. Vīllās fēminārum poētārum _____.
   (you love)

   It means _____

2. Agricolae tubās _____ hodiē occupant.
   (of the girls)

   It means _____

3. Locum portae vīllae diū _____.
   (you look at)

   It means _____

4. Captīvus lēgātum et sociōs _____.
   (fights)

   It means _____

5. Animum et _____ agricolae laudās.
   (the boldness)

   It means _____

☐ I practiced my flashcards today.

Latin Workbook - Level 3
Copyright © 1998 by Karen Mohs

LET'S PRACTICE

Write the meanings of these Latin sentences.

1. Agricola animōs servōrum iam parat.

   It means _____

2. Amīcum puellae pugnās, sed nōn socium.

   It means _____

3. Epistulās portāmus, et captīvōs appellāmus.

   It means _____

4. Nōn semper das causam fugae equōrum.

   It means _____

5. Nūntiō poenam populōrum et rēgīnārum.

   It means _____

6. Servōs servās, sed amīcōs nōn amās.

   It means _____

7. Equus portam spectat, et agricolam oppugnat.

   It means _____

8. Fābulam semper nārrās memoriārum nūntiōrum.

   It means _____

9. Puellae annōs cōpiae diū exspectant.

   It means _____

10. Amīcitiam prōvinciārum fīlī nōn superās.

    It means _____

☐ I practiced my flashcards today.

LET'S PRACTICE

Connect each key to the correct key ring.

Latin Workbook - Level 3
Copyright © 1998 by Karen Mohs

Puella habitat.   It means **The girl lives.**

Now let's tell *where* the girl lives.

In īnsulā puella habitat.

It means **The girl lives on the island.**

In lūdō puella habitat.

It means **The girl lives in the school.**

Now read these Latin sentences. Write what they mean.

1. In silvā habitāmus.

    It means _____

2. In campō pugnās.

    It means _____

Put a check in the box when you notice:

☐ The Latin word in can mean *in* or *on*.

☐ The new ending ā is used with words ending in a like the word īnsula.

☐ The new ending ō is used with words ending in us like the word lūdus.

☐ I practiced my flashcards today. (Add the new cards.)

LET'S PRACTICE

Match the Latin sentences to their meanings.

_____ 1. Fābulam in vīllā nārrō.   a. You tell the story in the villa.

_____ 2. Fābulam in vīllā nārrās.   b. She tells the stories in the villa.

_____ 3. Fābulās in vīllā nārrās.   c. We tell the stories in the villa.

_____ 4. Fābulās in vīllā nārrat.   d. I tell the story in the villa.

_____ 5. Fābulās in vīllā nārrāmus.   e. You tell the stories in the villa.

_____ 6. Exspectō filiōs in īnsulā.   f. He awaits the sons on the island.

_____ 7. In īnsulā filiōs exspectat.   g. You await the son on the island.

_____ 8. Exspectat filiōs īnsula.   h. I await the sons on the island.

_____ 9. Filiī exspectant īnsulam.   i. The sons await the island.

_____ 10. In īnsulā exspectās filium.   j. The island awaits the sons.

_____ 11. Sociōs in aquā vulnerō.   k. I wound the ally in the water.

_____ 12. In aquā socium vulnerō.   l. The water wounds the ally.

_____ 13. Sociōs in aquā vulnerat.   m. It wounds the allies in the water.

_____ 14. Vulnerat socium aqua.   n. The waters wound the allies.

_____ 15. Sociōs aquae vulnerant.   o. I wound the allies in the water.

☐ I practiced my flashcards today.

In īnsulā puella habitat. It means **The girl lives on the island.**
In lūdō puella habitat. It means **The girl lives in the school.**

Now for more than one!

In īnsulīs puella habitat. It means **The girl lives on the *islands*.**
In lūdīs puella habitat. It means **The girl lives in the *schools*.**

Now read these Latin sentences. Write what they mean.

1. In vīllīs pugnat.

   It means _____

2. In equīs labōrās.

   It means _____

Put a check in the box when you notice:

☐ The new plural ending īs is used with words ending in a like the word īnsula.

☐ The same plural ending īs is used with words ending in us like the word lūdus.

☐ I practiced my flashcards today. (Add the new cards.)

LET'S PRACTICE

Match the words to their meanings.

viās	road	in fābulā	in the story
viae	of the road	fābulam	of the stories
in viīs	roads	fābulae	stories
viam	on the roads	fābulārum	story
in viā	on the road	in fābulīs	in the stories
aquārum	in the waters	gladiī	of the sword
in aquā	of the waters	in gladiīs	swords
aquae	in the water	gladī	on the swords
aqua	waters	gladiōrum	on the sword
in aquīs	water	in gladiō	of the swords
carrī	of the carts	in vīllīs	farmhouse
carrus	carts	vīlla	in the farmhouses
carrōrum	cart	in vīllā	in the farmhouse
in carrīs	of the cart	vīllārum	farmhouses
carrōs	in the carts	vīllae	of the farmhouses

☐ I practiced my flashcards today.

Puellās convocō.   It means **I summon the girls.**

Now let's tell the ***means*** by which I summon the girls.

Puellās tubā convocō.

It means **I summon the girls on (by means of)* the trumpet.**

Puellās tubīs convocō.

It means **I summon the girls on (by means of)* the *trumpets*.**

Now read these Latin sentences. Write what they mean.

1. Lēgātōs gladiō pugnō.

   It means _____

2. Poētās laudant linguīs.

   It means _____

Put a check in the box when you notice:

☐ It is the ending alone, without additional words, that tells the means by which something is done.

☐ The endings are the same as the endings used with the Latin word in (which is used to show ***where*** something is done).

*As the student translates, he may use any of a number of prepositions (***with***, ***in***, ***on***, etc.), but he must remember that the idea of this construction is "by means of."

☐ I practiced my flashcards today. (Add the new cards.)

LET'S PRACTICE

Circle the correct Latin words.

with swords	with the trumpet	on the wagon
in gladiīs gladiō gladiīs	in tubā tubā tubīs	in carrō carrōrum in carrīs
on the horse	**in the carts**	**in the provinces**
equōs in equō in equīs	in carrīs in carrō carrus	in prōvinciā prōvinciae in prōvinciīs
on the street	**with rumors**	**on the gate**
viae in viīs in viā	in fāmīs fāmā fāmīs	in portā in portīs portās
forests	**in the country houses**	**with the trumpets**
silvā in silvīs silvae	in vīllīs in vīllā vīllam	tubīs tubās tubā
in the schools	**farmhouses**	**on the horses**
in lūdīs in lūdō lūdus	in vīllā vīllae vīllārum	in equō equī in equīs

☐ I practiced my flashcards today.

Pugnō.   It means **I fight.**

Now let's tell the *manner* in which I fight.

Cum audāciā pugnō.

It means **I fight with* boldness.**

Now read these Latin sentences. Write what they mean.

1. Cum dīligentiā labōrās.

   It means _____

2. Causam cum audāciā nūntiat.

   It means _____

3. Vocō cum amīcitiā agricolās.

   It means _____

Put a check in the box when you notice:

☐ When expressing the manner in which something is done, we use the Latin word cum.

☐ The endings are the same as the endings used with the Latin word in (which is used to show *where* something is done).

*As the student translates, he may use the preposition *with*, but he must remember that the idea of this construction is the *manner* in which a thing is done.

☐ I practiced my flashcards today. (Add the new card.)

LET'S PRACTICE

Write the meanings on the lines below the Latin sentences.

Cum dīligentiā pugnat.	Gladiōs cum audāciā portō.
_____	_____
Gladiīs pugnant.	Gladium in patriā portat.
_____	_____
In vīllā habitat.	Nautās tubā convocāmus.
_____	_____
Cum amīcitiā habitat.	Nautae fīliōs convocat.
_____	_____

Write the correct Latin words on the lines beside the meanings.

on the island _____

with friendliness _____

in the forests _____

with the trumpet _____

with diligence _____

with the swords _____

☐ I practiced my flashcards today.

Amās puellam.   It means **You like the girl.**

(when there is only one *you*)

Now for more than one *you*.

Amātis puellam.   It means **You like the girl.**

(when there are more than one *you*)

Color the block orange if the Latin word means only one *you*. Color it purple if the Latin word means more than one *you*.

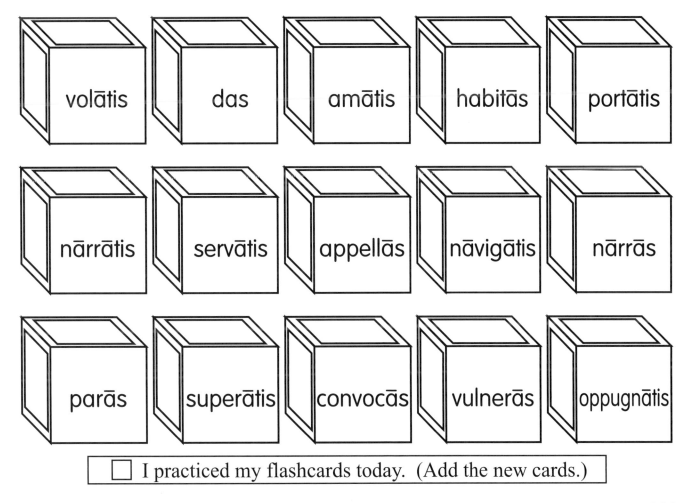

volātis   das   amātis   habitās   portātis

nārrātis   servātis   appellās   nāvigātis   nārrās

parās   superātis   convocās   vulnerās   oppugnātis

☐ I practiced my flashcards today. (Add the new cards.)

LET'S PRACTICE

Write the meanings of these Latin words.

amō _____   amāmus _____

amās _____   amātis _____

amat _____   amant _____

dō _____   damus _____

das _____   datis _____

dat _____   dant _____

volō _____   volāmus _____

volās _____   volātis _____

volat _____   volant _____

nārrō _____   nārrāmus _____

nārrās _____   nārrātis _____

nārrat _____   nārrant _____

☐ I practiced my flashcards today.

LET'S PRACTICE

Put checks in the boxes of the correct Latin sentences.

The girls in the farmhouse always look at the horses on the plain.
☐ Puella in vīllā equōs in campīs semper spectat.
☐ Puellae in vīllā equōs in campō semper spectant.
☐ Puellās in vīllārum equōs in campō semper spectat.
The lieutenants do not attack the ally with diligence.
☐ Lēgātī socium nōn oppugnāmus cum dīligentiīs.
☐ Lēgātus sociōs nōn oppugnat cum dīligentiā.
☐ Lēgātī socium nōn oppugnant cum dīligentiā.
We live for a long time in the native land, and we love the villas.
☐ In patriā diū habitāmus, et vīllās amāmus.
☐ In patriīs diū habitant, et vīllīs amant.
☐ In patriā diū habitō, et vīllās amō.
The poet's son defeats the tribes in the forest, and he wounds the captives.
☐ Filiī poēta populōs in silvā superant, et captīvōs vulnerat.
☐ Fīlius poētae populōs in silvā superat, et captīvōs vulnerat.
☐ Fīlius poētae populīs in silvīs superō, et captīvōs vulnerō.
You announce the news with boldness, but you do not love the country.
☐ Cum audāciā nūntium nūntiās, sed patriam nōn amās.
☐ In audāciā nūntium nūntiās, et patriās nōn amat.
☐ Cum audāciīs nūntium nūntiō, sed patriam nōn amāmus.

☐ I practiced my flashcards today.

Latin Workbook - Level 3
Copyright © 1998 by Karen Mohs

131

PUZZLE TIME

Find the hidden sentence. (Hint: It has three words.)

F	ē	m	l	a
ī	f	i	m	u
l	s	n	u	d
i	ā	ā	r	ō

Write the sentence.

_____

_ _

_____

It means _____

Match the Latin words to their meanings.

____ 1. nāvigant   a. you (plural) sail

____ 2. nāvigat   b. she sails

____ 3. nāvigāmus   c. you (singular) sail

____ 4. nāvigās   d. they sail

____ 5. nāvigātis   e. we sail

☐ I practiced my flashcards today.

132

Carrum dō.   It means **I give the cart.**

Now let's tell *to whom* I give the cart.

Puellae* carrum dō.   It means **I give the cart *to the girl.***
or
I give the cart *for the girl.*

Fīliō** carrum dō.   It means **I give the cart *to the son.***
or
I give the cart *for the son.*

Circle the correct Latin words. Then write what the sentences mean.

1. Puella
   Puellae aquam in carrō hodiē das.

   It means _____

2. Nūntiāmus agricolae
   agricola in equō audāciam fīlī.

   It means _____

3. In silvā lēgātō
   lēgātus tubam semper portō.

   It means _____

*Notice that the ending ae (on words like puella), in this case meaning *to* or *for* the girl, is identical to the ending of two other uses: the plural subject (the girls *doing* the action) and the singular possessive (**belonging to** the girl). (See pages 83 and 39.)

**Notice that the ending ō (on words like fīlius), in this case meaning *to* or *for* the son, is identical to the ending of another use: the place *where*. (See page 121.)

☐ I practiced my flashcards today. (Add the new cards.)

LET'S PRACTICE

Match the correct spelling of the Latin words to the sentences. Some answers may be used more than once.

_____ 1. The friend *of the girl* is here.

_____ 2. The mother gives *the girl* a bowl.

_____ 3. The friend *of the girls* is here.

_____ 4. The farmer looks at *the girls*.

_____ 5. *The girls* look at the farmer.

a. puellae
b. puellārum
c. puellās

_____ 6. The friend *of the son* has a horse.

_____ 7. The father hands *the son* a plow.

_____ 8. *The sons* like the boy.

_____ 9. The boy likes *the son*.

d. fīlium
e. fīlī
f. fīliī
g. fīliō

_____ 10. She gave *the friend* a flower.

_____ 11. The daughter *of the friend* is young.

_____ 12. *The friend* smells the flowers.

_____ 13. *The friends* smell the flowers.

_____ 14. The girl has two *friends*.

h. amīcōs
i. amīcō
j. amīcī
k. amīcus

☐ I practiced my flashcards today.

LET'S PRACTICE

Fill in the blanks with the correct Latin words. Then write what the sentences mean.

1. Puella _____ fāmās semper nūntiat.
   _____
   (to the queen)

   It means _____

2. Damus hodiē agricolae carrōs et _____.
                                    _____
                                    (the horses)

   It means _____

3. In aquīs īnsulae _____ fēminārum nāvigant.
                    _____
                    (the sons)

   It means _____

4. Animī poētārum _____ fābulās nunc parant.
                  _____
                  (for the son)

   It means _____

5. Epistulam exspectātis, et amīcōs _____ vocātis.
                                    _____
                                    (of the slaves)

   It means _____

☐ I practiced my flashcards today.

LET'S PRACTICE

Write the meanings of these Latin sentences.

1. Amīcō nūntī amīcitiam populī nūntiātis.

    It means _____

2. Equus aquam prōvinciae amat, sed aquam silvae nōn amat.

    It means _____

3. Sociō puellae nūntiōs hodiē nārrāmus.

    It means _____

4. Memoriae dēlectant filiōs et filiās in īnsulā.

    It means _____

5. Captīvum in vīllā gladiō servō.

    It means _____

6. Laudās dīligentiam lēgātōrum in campō.

    It means _____

7. Amīcō puellae carrōs fēminae nōn datis.

    It means _____

8. Vocant filiī lēgātōs in campīs et in viīs.

    It means _____

9. Cum audāciā socius in silvīs prōvinciae pugnat.

    It means _____

10. Exspectāmus poenam et fugam lēgātōrum rēgīnae.

    It means _____

☐ I practiced my flashcards today.

Puellae carrum dō.   It means **I give the cart *to the girl.***
or
I give the cart *for the girl.*

Now for more than one!

Puellīs* carrum dō.   It means **I give the cart *to the girls.***
or
I give the cart *for the girls.*

Fīliō carrum dō.   It means **I give the cart *to the son.***
or
I give the cart *for the son.*

Again . . . more than one!

Fīliīs* carrum dō.   It means **I give the cart *to the sons.***
or
I give the cart *for the sons.*

Put a check in the box when you notice:

☐ This plural ending (īs) is the same for words like puella and words like fīlius.

*This ending (īs) is identical to the plural ending used to show the place *where*. (See page 123.)

☐ I practiced my flashcards today. (Add the new cards.)

LET'S PRACTICE

Circle the correct Latin words.

1. (Puellae, **Puellīs**) carrum damus.

   It means **We give the cart to the girl.**

2. (**Puellae**, Puellīs) carrum damus.

   It means **We give the cart to the girls.**

---

3. Agricolae (equō, **equīs**) aquam portant.

   It means **The farmers carry water for the horses.**

4. Agricolae (**equō**, equīs) aquam portant.

   It means **The farmers carry water for the horse.**

---

5. (Lēgātō, **Lēgātīs**) rēgīnae gladiōs parātis.

   It means **You prepare the swords for the queen's envoys.**

6. (**Lēgātō**, Lēgātīs) rēgīnae gladiōs parātis.

   It means **You prepare the swords for the queen's envoy.**

---

7. Amīcus puellārum (**fīliae**, fīliīs) equum dat.

   It means **The friend of the girls gives the daughter a horse.**

8. Amīcus puellārum (fīliae, **fīliīs**) equum dat.

   It means **The friend of the girls gives the daughters a horse.**

☐ I practiced my flashcards today.

LET'S PRACTICE

Choose the correct words for the sentences. Put them in the blanks.
Then write what the sentences mean.

| audācia - audācia |

1. Fīliōs cum _____ superās.

It means _____

| Fīlius - Fīliō |

2. _____ tubās dant.

It means _____

| īnsulae - īnsulā |

3. Portās nautam in _____.

It means _____

| amīcitiā - amīcitiam |

4. Fīliās cum _____ spectātis.

It means _____

| nūntī - nūntiī |

5. In vīllā _____ habitat.

It means _____

| poēta - poētae |

6. Dō _____ epistulās.

It means _____

| Animīs - Animōs |

7. _____ captīvōrum laudat.

It means _____

☐ I practiced my flashcards today.

LET'S PRACTICE

Choose the best words for the sentences below. Then write what the sentences mean.

silvās	silvā	silva

1. In _____ equus servōs agricolae oppugnat.

   It means _____

2. In īnsulā in aquā _____ est.

   It means _____

3. Populī _____ nātūrae hodiē nōn amant.

   It means _____

appellat	appellātis	appellant

1. Agricola portās vīllae _____.

   It means _____

2. Nūntiī _____ agricolās in vīllīs.

   It means _____

3. Vīllās agricolārum _____.

   It means _____

☐ I practiced my flashcards today.

cūra

means

care, anxiety

Write the Latin word that means **care**.

Write the Latin word that means **I stand**.

stō

means

I stand

saepe

means

often

Write the Latin word that means **often**.

☐ I practiced my flashcards today. (Add the new cards.)

LET'S PRACTICE

Write the meanings of these Latin words.

poena _____   animus _____

stāmus _____   socius _____

fuga _____   vulnerō _____

exspectat _____   locus _____

dīligentia _____   dēlectant _____

servātis _____   puer _____

fābula _____   habitat _____

nārrant _____   captīvus _____

audācia _____   nūntius _____

volō _____   temptāmus _____

saepe _____   cūra _____

carrus _____   populus _____

amicus _____   ager _____

superās _____   oppugnātis _____

cōpia _____   crās _____

lībērō

means

**I set free,
I free**

Write the Latin word that means **I free**.

_____

_____

_____

_____

Write the Latin word that means **meanwhile**.

_____

_____

_____

_____

interim

means

meanwhile

cūr

means

why
(a question)

Write the Latin word that means **why?**

_____

_____

_____

_____

☐ I practiced my flashcards today. (Add the new cards.)

LET'S PRACTICE

Choose the correct words for the sentences. Put them in the blanks.
Then write what the sentences mean.

cūr - stāmus

1. In aquā interim _____.

It means _____

īnsula - īnsulās

2. Captīvōs in _____ līberās.

It means _____

Gladiīs - Gladiī

3. _____ nōn saepe pugnō.

It means _____

poētārum - poētās

4. Cūr _____ oppugnātis?

It means _____

puellīs - puellās

5. Quid _____ semper dat?

It means _____

viā - viae

6. Nūntium in _____ nūntiant.

It means _____

carrus - carrōs

7. Servātis cum dīligentiā _____.

It means _____

☐ I practiced my flashcards today.

144

dēmōnstrō

means

**I point out,
I show**

Write the Latin word that means **I show**.

_____

_____

_____

Write the Latin word that means **hour**.

_____

_____

_____

hōra

means

hour

posteā

means

**after that time,
afterward, thereafter**

Write the Latin word that means **afterward**.

_____

_____

_____

☐ I practiced my flashcards today. (Add the new cards.)

LET'S PRACTICE

Color the box pink if the English meaning matches the Latin word at the beginning of the row.

cōpia	supplies	supply	for the supplies
gladiī	of the sword	swords	sword
dēmōnstrāmus	we show	you show	they show
līberat	she frees	they free	I free
cūra	of anxiety	anxieties	anxiety
stās	it stands	you stand	we stand
posteā	thereafter	meanwhile	tomorrow
vītārum	of the life	of the lives	lives
volātis	you fly	he flies	they fly
hōrās	of the hour	hour	hours

☐ I practiced my flashcards today.

inopia

means

want, lack, need, poverty

Write the Latin word that means **want**.

_____

_____

_____

_____

Write the Latin word that means **wealth**.

_____

_____

_____

_____

pecūnia

means

wealth, money

cōnfīrmō

means

I strengthen, I encourage, I declare

Write the Latin word that means **I declare**.

_____

_____

_____

_____

☐ I practiced my flashcards today. (Add the new cards.)

LET'S PRACTICE

Write the Latin words.

yesterday	it likes
what?	I defeat
with	where?
we fly	we stand
tomorrow	I report
I fight	they call
she tells	of the sons
but	I keep
we grant	already
afterward	why?
of the streets	long
they praise	he carries

☐ I practiced my flashcards today.

148

tum

means

**then,
at that time**

Write the Latin word that means **then**.

_____

_____

_____

Write the Latin word that means **I shout**.

_____

_____

_____

clāmō

means

I shout

dominus

means

**master,
Lord, owner**

Write the Latin word that means **master**.

_____

_____

_____

☐ I practiced my flashcards today. (Add the new cards.)

LET'S PRACTICE

Match the words to their meanings.

dominus	owners	hōrārum	of the hours
locōs	owner	convocō	they please
lūdum	places	dēlectant	I assemble
dominī	play	dominīs	to the masters
liberātis	you free	spectāmus	you live
filiō	to the daughter	est	of the need
filiae	to the son	inopiae	there is
volāmus	we fly	habitās	we look at
cūrae	hours	animōs	you shout
pecūnia	of anxiety	animum	minds
temptant	they attempt	clāmātis	spirit
hōrae	wealth	tum	I point out
pecūniae	she frees	dēmōnstrō	now
nāvigās	of the money	iam	at that time
liberat	you sail	linguās	languages

☐ I practiced my flashcards today.

ambulō

means

**I stroll,
I walk**

Write the Latin word that means **I walk**.

- -

_____

- -

_____

- -

Write the Latin word that means **badly**.

- -

_____

- -

_____

- -

male

means

**badly,
insufficiently**

numerus

means

**number,
group**

Write the Latin word that means **number**.

- -

_____

- -

_____

- -

☐ I practiced my flashcards today. (Add the new cards.)

LET'S PRACTICE

Color the box brown if the Latin word matches the English meaning at the beginning of the row.

they show	dēmōnstrat	dēmōnstrō	dēmōnstrant
badly	cūr	tum	male
I shout	clāmāmus	clāmō	clāmās
we set free	līberāmus	līberātis	līberant
master	dominī	dominus	dominōs
he stands	stāmus	stant	stat
poverty	inopia	inopiae	inopiās
you stroll	ambulāmus	ambulātis	ambulō
money	pecūniae	pecūnia	pecūniās
you declare	cōnfirmant	cōnfirmāmus	cōnfirmās

☐ I practiced my flashcards today.

LET'S PRACTICE

Write the Latin words.

reason _____

hour _____

often _____

we shout _____

badly _____

he
attempts _____

thereafter _____

we free _____

he
reports _____

I walk _____

penalty _____

they keep _____

she
labors _____

meanwhile _____

they are _____

then _____

I declare _____

tomorrow _____

he
summons _____

we like _____

group _____

why? _____

we fly _____

anxiety _____

☐ I practiced my flashcards today.

LET'S PRACTICE

Match the words to their meanings.

dominīs	owners		līberō	he frees
dominus	to the owners		līberātis	you free
dominī	owner		līberat	I free
nāvigātis	he sails		volāmus	you fly
nāvigāmus	we sail		volātis	they fly
nāvigat	you sail		volant	we fly
ambulant	we walk		habitātis	you live
ambulāmus	you walk		habitāmus	it lives
ambulātis	they walk		habitat	we live
spectat	he looks at		hōra	hours
spectant	you look at		hōrārum	hour
spectātis	they look at		hōrae	of the hours
vulnerant	I wound		clāmat	she shouts
vulnerō	they wound		clāmant	they shout
vulnerātis	you wound		clāmās	you shout

☐ I practiced my flashcards today.

154

Latin Workbook - Level 3
Copyright © 1998 by Karen Mohs

LET'S PRACTICE

Color the box orange if the English meaning matches the Latin word at the beginning of the row.

numerī	of the group	group	for the group
locī	of the places	place	places
inopia	poverty	of poverty	for poverty
dominōrum	of the lords	for the lords	lords
captīvō	captive	of the captive	to the captive
rēgīnae	queen	for the queen	of the queens
puellīs	girl	to the girl	to the girls
male	insufficiently	for a long time	along with
pecūniam	wealth	of wealth	for wealth
hōrās	of hours	hour	hours

☐ I practiced my flashcards today.

LET'S PRACTICE

Color the popsicle purple if the words inside mean the same.

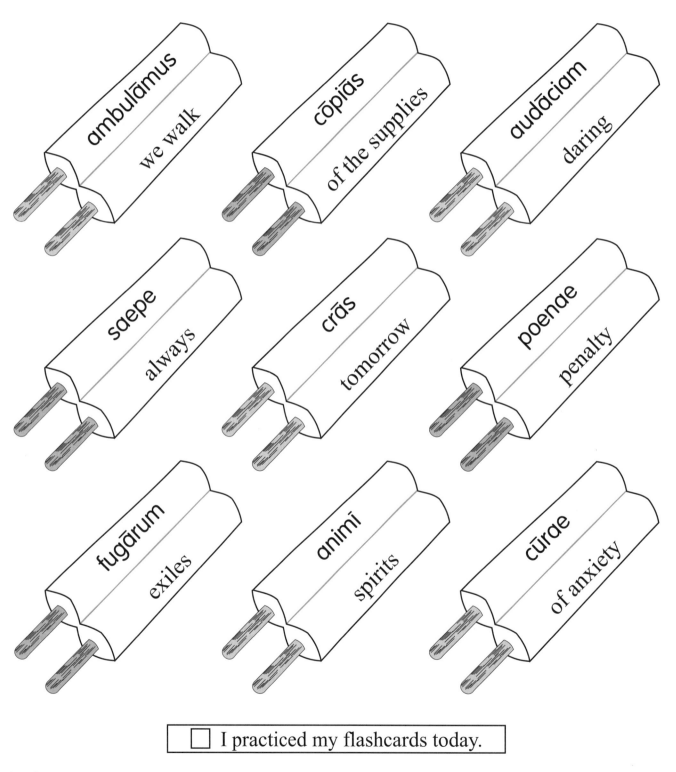

I practiced my flashcards today.

LET'S PRACTICE

Put checks in the boxes of the correct Latin sentences.

You always shout the news of the hour to the captives in the cart.
☐ Captīvīs in carrō nūntium hōrae semper clāmātis.
☐ Captīvō in carrīs nūntium hōrae semper clāmātis.
☐ Captīvīs in carrō nūntium hōrae semper clāmāmus.

The poet walks on the road and prepares for the game with care.
☐ Poētae in viā ambulant et lūdum cum dīligentiā parant.
☐ Poēta in viā ambulat et lūdum cum dīligentiā parat.
☐ Poēta in viīs ambulat et lūdās cum dīligentiā parat.

We stand on the plain and look at the farmer's horses and villas.
☐ In campīs stāt et equōs et vīllās agricolae spectāt.
☐ In campō stāmus et equus et vīlla agricolae spectāmus.
☐ In campō stāmus et equōs et vīllās agricolae spectāmus.

The daughters please the women, but the sons point out the reasons.
☐ Fīlia fēminās dēlectat, sed fīliī causās dēmōnstrant.
☐ Fīliī fēminās dēlectant, sed fīliae causās dēmōnstrant.
☐ Fīliae fēminās dēlectant, sed fīliī causās dēmōnstrant.

Why do the friends on the island attack the sailors in the forest with swords?
☐ Cūr amīcī in īnsulā nautās in silvā gladiīs oppugnant?
☐ Ubi amīcī in īnsulā nautās in silvā gladiīs oppugnant?
☐ Cum amīcī in īnsulā nautās in silvā gladiīs oppugnant?

☐ I practiced my flashcards today.

LET'S PRACTICE

Put the endings in the boxes on the Latin words in the sentences.

ārum ō	1. Cōnfirm_ numer__ fēmin____.	
ōrum ōs	It means **I encourage the groups of women.**	

ātis ōs	2. Captīv_ cum audāci_ nunc līber____.	
āmus ā	It means **We now free the captives with boldness.**	

ās ōs	3. Poēt__ port__ et viās dēmōnstr__.	
ās ae	It means **You show the poet the gates and streets.**	

ās us	4. Ubi fīli__ lēgāt__ vulner__?	
at um	It means **Where does the son wound the envoy?**	

at ae	5. Quid naut__ agricol_ d__?	
a ā	It means **What does the farmer give to the sailor?**	

ae at	6. Lingu___ patri__ laud__.	
ant am	It means **She praises the language of the native land.**	

☐ I practiced my flashcards today.

158

LET'S PRACTICE

Fill in the blanks with the correct words from the boxes on the right.
Then write the meanings of the sentences.

1. Occupāmus _____ gladiō.

   It means _____

captīvus
captīvum
captīvōrum

2. Puella in terrā rēgīnae _____.

   It means _____

habitat
habitō
habitant

3. Cum amīcitiā fābulam _____.

   It means _____

nautās
nārrant
nūntiārum

4. _____ filī tubās dō.

   It means _____

Amīcīs
Amīcus
Amīcās

5. Lūdōs puellārum in _____ laudās.

   It means _____

villā
villa
villae

6. Cūr _____ hodiē convocātis?

   It means _____

populus
populōrum
populōs

7. Lēgātus gladiōs in equō _____.

   It means _____

portāmus
portat
portant

☐ I practiced my flashcards today.

LET'S PRACTICE

Choose the best words for the sentences below. Then write what the sentences mean.

spectat	spectant	spectās

_____

1. Inopiam numerōrum servōrum in prōvinciā _____.

   It means _____

   _____

2. Cūr fēmina _____ terram agricolārum?

   It means _____

   _____

3. Nautae semper _____ aquās īnsulārum.

   It means _____

fīliīs	fīlia	fīliae

   _____

1. Dominīs _____ fābulās carrōrum nārrat.

   It means _____

   _____

2. Das _____ poētārum tubam.

   It means _____

   _____

3. Interim _____ captīvōrum in viīs stant.

   It means _____

☐ I practiced my flashcards today.

160

FINAL REVIEW

Match the words to their meanings.

porta	I shout	fāma	owner
spectō	gate	dominus	reputation
clāmō	I look at	nūntius	water
amīcus	friend	aqua	I keep
fuga	I address	servō	message
appellō	often	īnsula	along with
saepe	situation	nārrō	island
locus	exile	cum	I relate
captīvus	captive	nāvigō	I sail
fābula	sword	nauta	sailor
dīligentia	I wound	cūr	letter
gladius	story	littera	why?
vulnerō	care	patria	plain
fortūna	I praise	exspectō	I wait for
servus	chance	campus	country
sed	but	dēmōnstrō	nature
laudō	slave	vīlla	horse
prōvincia	hour	nātūra	country house
hōra	province	equus	I show

☐ I practiced my flashcards today.

FINAL REVIEW

Match the words to their meanings.

agricola	also	labōrō	for a long time
habitō	game	amīcitia	I suffer
lūdus	I dwell	diū	friendliness
et	farmer	pecūnia	money
līberō	poet	poena	I declare
poēta	I free	cōnfirmō	punishment
herī	life	ad	I prepare for
vīta	now	parō	what?
nunc	yesterday	quid	to
vocō	I try	populus	boy
annus	year	puer	she is
temptō	I call	superō	people
epistula	epistle	est	I defeat
terra	wagon	socius	language
hodiē	earth	stō	I stand
occupō	today	lingua	comrade
carrus	I capture	posteā	mind
audācia	daring	animus	thereafter

☐ I practiced my flashcards today.

Latin Workbook - Level 3
Copyright © 1998 by Karen Mohs

FINAL REVIEW

Match the words to their meanings.

tum	where?	nōn	not
oppugnō	then	portō	forest
puella	I attack	silva	I carry
ubi	girl	dēlectō	street
dō	I walk	via	always
memoria	memory	semper	I please
ambulō	I grant	filia	on
amō	I like	causa	reason
cōpia	son	in	daughter
filius	supply	lēgātus	envoy
crās	tomorrow	convocō	I assemble
sunt	queen	inopia	meanwhile
cūra	they are	interim	need
rēgīna	anxiety	ager	woman
volō	already	numerus	group
iam	trumpet	male	badly
tuba	I fly	fēmina	field
nūntiō	I report	pugnō	I fight

☐ I practiced my flashcards today.

FINAL REVIEW

Draw pictures for these sentences.

Poētae in patriā saepe ambulant, et fīliōs fēminārum laudant.

Cum audāciā nūntium clāmāmus, sed poenam nōn amāmus.

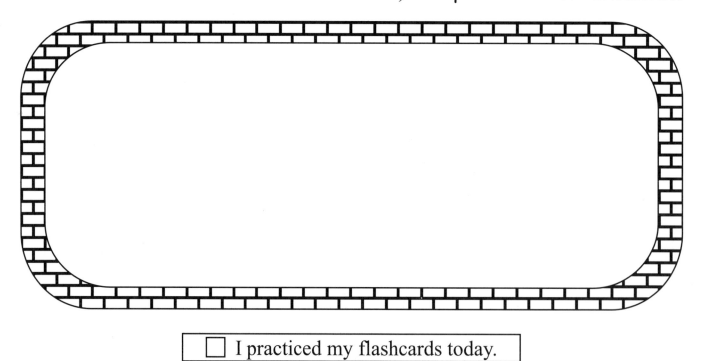

☐ I practiced my flashcards today.

FINAL REVIEW

Match the correct Latin sentences to their meanings below.

a. Cūr in īnsulīs diū habitō?

b. Quid fēminae in aquā tum exspectant?

c. Cūr in carrīs servōs semper līberātis?

d. Ubi volātis et ubi ambulātis?

e. Cūr amīcus iam oppugnat prōvinciam?

f. Quid fīliīs sociōrum datis?

g. Ubi lēgātī inopiās populōrum cōnfirmant?

h. Cūr rēgīnae poētās in silvīs servant?

( ) 1. What do you give to the sons of the comrades?

( ) 2. Where do you fly, and where do you walk?

( ) 3. Why do the queens keep the poets in the forests?

( ) 4. What do the women in the water wait for at that time?

( ) 5. Why do I dwell on the islands for a long time?

( ) 6. Why does the friend attack the province already?

( ) 7. Where do the envoys declare the needs of the nations?

( ) 8. Why do you always free the slaves in the wagons?

☐ I practiced my flashcards today.

FINAL REVIEW

Write the meanings of these Latin words.

dēlectō _____	dēlectāmus _____
dēlectās _____	dēlectātis _____
dēlectat _____	dēlectant _____

vīlla _____	vīllae _____
vīllae _____	vīllārum _____
vīllae _____	vīllīs _____
vīllam _____	vīllās _____
in vīllā _____	in vīllīs _____

clāmō _____	clāmāmus _____
clāmās _____	clāmātis _____
clāmat _____	clāmant _____

locus _____	locī _____
locī _____	locōrum _____
locō _____	locīs _____
locum _____	locōs _____
in locō _____	in locīs _____

☐ I practiced my flashcards today.

FINAL REVIEW

Write the sentences using the words on the right.

1. _____

It means **We stand on the horse.**

2. _____

It means **The horses stand in the water.**

3. _____

It means **You stand and carry the water.**

aquā
aquam
equī
equō
et
in
in
portās
stāmus
stant
stās

4. _____

It means **I shout to the son.**

5. _____

It means **The sons shout to the friends.**

amīcīs
amīcus
clāmant
clāmat
clāmō
fīlī
fīliī
fīliō

6. _____

It means **The friend of the son shouts.**

☐ I practiced my flashcards today.

FINAL REVIEW

Color the butterfly if the words on its wings mean the same.

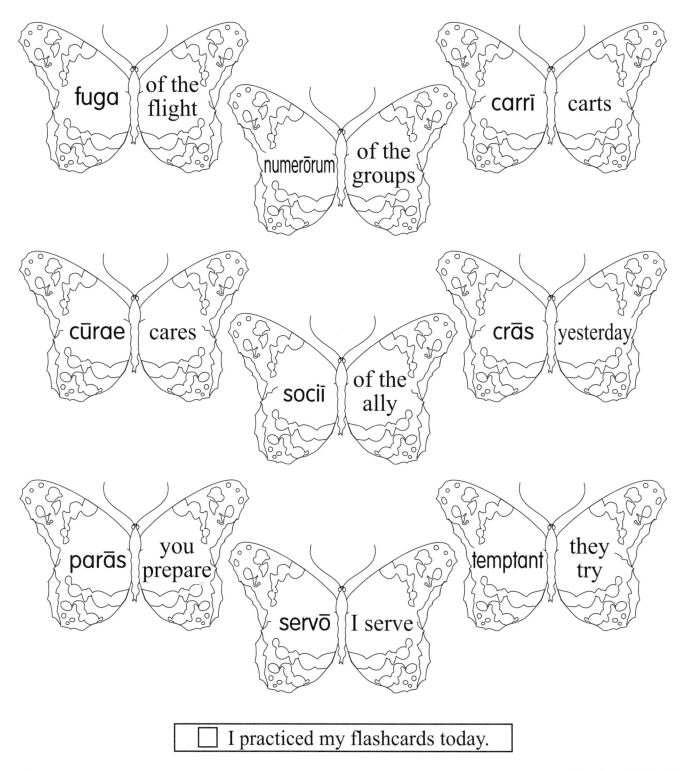

I practiced my flashcards today.

FINAL REVIEW

Write the meanings of these Latin sentences.

1. Cūr lēgātōs gladiīs oppugnāmus?

   It means _____

2. Hōram poenae diū exspectātis.

   It means _____

3. Fēminīs nautārum epistulās nunc damus.

   It means _____

4. Dominō prōvinciās in terrā hodiē dēmōnstrō.

   It means _____

5. Captīvus in carrō stat, et populō clāmat.

   It means _____

6. Numerī filiārum semper cōnfirmant in īnsulā agricolās.

   It means _____

7. Portam in equō cum dīligentiā interim portātis.

   It means _____

8. Cūr agricolae in campīs rēginīs terrae labōrant?

   It means _____

9. Ubi filius poētae servat pecūniam et aquam?

   It means _____

10. Posteā lēgātī male pugnant, et rēginam nōn amant.

    It means _____

☐ I practiced my flashcards today.

PUZZLE TIME

Think of the meanings of the English words. Then write the Latin words on the puzzle below.

across	down
3. on	1. I attack
7. wealth	2. why?
8. I dwell	3. already
9. I love	4. language
10. I stand	5. I give
12. where?	6. friendship
15. now	8. hour
16. boldness	11. flight
18. reason	13. poverty
19. penalty	14. insufficiently
22. I walk	17. anxiety
23. reputation	20. to
24. often	21. then

I practiced my flashcards today.

170

APPENDIX

Latin - English Glossary

a

ad - to, near, toward, for, at (14)
ager - field, territory (17)
agricola - farmer (12)
ambulō - I stroll, I walk (151)
amīcitia - friendship, friendliness (22)
amīcus - friend (17)
amō - I love, I like (22)
animus - mind, spirit (105)
annus - year (23)
appellō - I address, I call, I name (43)
aqua - water (12)
audācia - boldness, daring (103)

c

campus - field, plain (19)
captivus - captive (101)
carrus - cart, wagon (105)
causa - cause, reason (53)
clāmō - I shout (149)
cōnfirmō - I strengthen, I encourage, I declare (147)
convocō - I call together, I assemble, I summon (55)
cōpia - plenty, supply (93)
crās - tomorrow (105)
cum - along with, with (20)
cūr - why? (143)
cūra - care, anxiety (141)

d

dēlectō - I please (53)
dēmōnstrō - I point out, I show (145)
dīligentia - diligence, care (55)
diū - for a long time, long (95)

do - I give, I grant (11)
dominus - master, Lord, owner (149)

e

epistula - letter, epistle (49)
equus - horse (22)
est - he is, she is, it is, there is (12)
et - and, also, even (13)
exspectō - I await, I wait for (49)

f

fābula - story (51)
fāma - report, rumor, reputation (47)
fēmina - woman, wife (12)
filia - daughter (21)
filius - son (21)
fortūna - fortune, chance, luck (16)
fuga - flight, exile (97)

g

gladius - sword (24)

h

habitō - I live, I dwell (51)
herī - yesterday (99)
hodiē - today (103)
hōra - hour (145)

i

iam - now, already (97)
in - into, against, in, on (93)
inopia - want, lack, need, poverty (147)
īnsula - island (13)
interim - meanwhile (143)

l

labōrō - I labor, I suffer, I am hard pressed (53)
laudō - I praise (14)
lēgātus - lieutenant, envoy (43)
liberō - I set free, I free (143)
lingua - tongue, language (22)
littera - letter (of the alphabet); (if plural: epistle, letter) (20)
locus - place, location, situation (101)
lūdus - game, play, school (43)

m

male - badly, insufficiently (151)
memoria - memory (15)

n

nārrō - I relate, I tell (47)
nātūra - nature (19)
nauta - sailor (20)
nāvigō - I sail (15)
nōn - not (14)
numerus - number, group (151)
nunc - now (51)
nūntiō - I announce, I report (45)
nūntius - messenger, message, news (45)

o

occupō - I seize, I capture (19)
oppugnō - I attack (95)

p

parō - I prepare, I prepare for (17)
patria - country, native land (21)
pecūnia - wealth, money (147)
poena - penalty, punishment (99)

Note: The number in parentheses indicates the page on which the vocabulary word is introduced.

APPENDIX

Latin - English Glossary

poēta - poet (23)
populus - people, nation, tribe (47)
porta - gate (15)
portō - I carry (16)
posteā - after that time, afterward, thereafter (145)
prōvincia - province (24)
puella - girl (11)
puer - boy (11)
pugnō - I fight (23)

q
quid - what? (16)

r
rēgīna - queen (49)

s
saepe - often (141)
sed - but (15)
semper - always (101)
servō - I guard, I save, I keep (99)
servus - slave (45)
silva - forest (13)
socius - comrade, ally (55)
spectō - I look at (19)
stō - I stand (141)
sunt - they are, there are (13)
superō - I surpass, I defeat (93)

t
temptō - I try, I attempt (97)
terra - earth, land, country (23)
tuba - trumpet (17)
tum - then, at that time (149)

u
ubi - where? (21)

v
via - road, way, street (16)
vīlla - farmhouse, country house, villa (20)
vīta - life (14)
vocō - I call (11)
volō - I fly (103)
vulnerō - I wound (95)

172

APPENDIX

English - Latin Glossary

a

address - appellō
after that time - posteā
afterward - posteā
against - in
ally - socius
along with - cum
already - iam
also - et
always - semper
and - et
announce - nūntiō
anxiety - cūra
are - sunt
assemble - convocō
at - ad
at that time - tum
attack - oppugnō
attempt - temptō
await - exspectō

b

badly - male
boldness - audācia
boy - puer
but - sed

c

call - vocō, appellō
call together - convocō
captive - captīvus
capture - occupō
care - dīligentia, cūra
carry - portō
cart - carrus
cause - causa
chance - fortūna
comrade - socius
country - patria, terra

country house - vīlla

d

daring - audācia
daughter - filia
declare - cōnfirmō
defeat - superō
diligence - dīligentia
dwell - habitō

e

earth - terra
encourage - cōnfirmō
envoy - lēgātus
epistle - littera (plural), epistula
even - et
exile - fuga

f

farmer - agricola
farmhouse - vīlla
field - ager, campus
fight - pugnō
flight - fuga
fly - volō
for - ad
for a long time - diū
forest - silva
fortune - fortūna
free - līberō
friend - amīcus
friendliness - amīcitia
friendship - amīcitia

g

game - lūdus
gate - porta
girl - puella
give - dō

grant - dō
group - numerus
guard - servō

h

hard pressed - labōrō
horse - equus
hour - hōra

i

in - in
insufficiently - male
into - in
is - est
island - īnsula

k

keep - servō

l

labor - labōrō
lack - inopia
land - terra
language - lingua
letter - littera, epistula
lieutenant - lēgātus
life - vīta
like - amō
live - habitō
location - locus
long - diū
look at - spectō
Lord - dominus
love - amō
luck - fortūna

m

master - dominus
meanwhile - interim

APPENDIX

English - Latin Glossary

memory - memoria
message - nūntius
messenger - nūntius
mind - animus
money - pecūnia

n
name - appellō
nation - populus
native land - patria
nature - nātūra
near - ad
need - inopia
news - nūntius
not - nōn
now - nunc, iam
number - numerus

o
often - saepe
on - in
owner - dominus

p
penalty - poena
people - populus
place - locus
plain - campus
play - lūdus
please - dēlectō
plenty - cōpia
poet - poēta
point out - dēmōnstrō
poverty - inopia
praise - laudō
prepare - parō
prepare for - parō
province - prōvincia
punishment - poena

q
queen - rēgīna

r
reason - causa
relate - nārrō
report - nūntiō, fāma
reputation - fāma
road - via
rumor - fāma

s
sail - nāvigō
sailor - nauta
save - servō
school - lūdus
seize - occupō
set free - līberō
shout - clāmō
show - dēmōnstrō
situation - locus
slave - servus
son - fīlius
spirit - animus
stand - stō
story - fābula
street - via
strengthen - cōnfirmō
stroll - ambulō
suffer - labōrō
summon - convocō
supply - cōpia
surpass - superō
sword - gladius

t
tell - nārrō
territory - ager
then - tum

thereafter - posteā
to - ad
today - hodiē
tomorrow - crās
tongue - lingua
toward - ad
tribe - populus
trumpet - tuba
try - temptō

v
villa - vīlla

w
wagon - carrus
wait for - exspectō
walk - ambulō
want - inopia
water - aqua
way - via
wealth - pecūnia
what? - quid
where? - ubi
why? - cūr
wife - fēmina
with - cum
woman - fēmina
wound - vulnerō

y
year - annus
yesterday - herī

APPENDIX

Latin Alphabet

Capital Letter	Small Letter	Pronunciation	Capital Letter	Small Letter	Pronunciation
Ā	ā	**a** in *father*	N	n	**n** in *nut*
A	a	**a** in *idea*	Ō**	ō**	**o** in *note*
B	b	**b** in *boy*	O**	o**	**o** in *omit*
C	c	**c** in *cat*	P	p	**p** in *pit*
D	d	**d** in *dog*	Q	q	**qu** in *quit*
Ē	ē	**ey** in *obey*	R	r	**r** in *run*
E	e	**e** in *bet*	S	s	**s** in *sit*
F	f	**f** in *fan*	T	t	**t** in *tag*
G	g	**g** in *go*	Ū	ū	**u** in *rule*
H	h	**h** in *hat*	U	u	**u** in *put*
Ī	ī	**i** in *machine*	V	v	**w** in *way*
I*	i*	**i** in *sit*	X	x	**ks** in *socks*
K	k	**k** in *king*	Ȳ	ȳ	form lips to say "**oo**" but say "**ee**" instead (held longer)
L	l	**l** in *land*	Y	y	form lips to say "**oo**" but say "**ee**" instead (held shorter)
M	m	**m** in *man*	Z	z	**dz** in *adze*

*When functioning as a consonant, i has the sound of **y** in *youth*. (See **Special Consonants** below.)
**The ō and the o both have a long o sound, but the ō is held longer.

Special Sounds

Diphthongs

Letters	Pronunciation
ae	*aye*
au	**ow** in *now*
ei	**ei** in *neighbor*
eu	*ay-oo*
oe	**oy** in *joy*
ui	**uee** in *queen*

Special Consonants

Letters	Pronunciation
bs	*ps*
bt	*pt*
ch	**ch** in *character*
gu	**gu** in *anguish*
i	**y** in *youth*
ph	**ph** in *phone*
su	**su** in *suave*
th	**th** in *thick*

APPENDIX

Word Order

Word order in Latin is not the same as word order in English. In Latin, since the ending determines the role the word plays in the sentence, word order is generally used for emphasis. However, there is a tendency to put the verb last.

Moods of the Latin Verb

Latin verbs are classified according to mood.

The **indicative** *mood* is used to make an assertion or to ask a question.
The **subjunctive** *mood* is used to describe an action that is not real.
The **imperative** *mood* is used to make a command.

A **participle** is a verbal adjective, and an **infinitive** is a verbal noun.

Voices of the Latin Verb

Voices of the Latin verb:

Active Voice: The subject of the sentence is *doing an action*.
Example: The man loves the woman.

Passive Voice: The subject of the sentence is *receiving an action*.
Example: The man is being loved by the woman.

Gender and Case of the Latin Noun

The three genders of Latin nouns are masculine, feminine, and neuter.

Latin nouns are declined using five main *cases*.

The subject of the sentence as well as a noun "linked" to the subject with a linking verb (e.g. *is* or *are*) belong in the **nominative** case. Possession is expressed with the **genitive** case. The indirect object belongs in the **dative** case. The direct object belongs in the **accusative** case. The **ablative** case is used to express special relationships. These cases have other important uses as well.

APPENDIX

First Conjugation

A Latin verb belongs to the first conjugation if its second principal part ends in -āre. Its present tense stem can be found by dropping the -re of the second principal part. (Principal parts will be taught later in this series.) The **present tense** is used to describe actions happening in the present time.

Present Active Indicative
(present indicative verb stem + personal ending)

	Singular	Meaning	Plural	Meaning
1st Person	amō	I like (*or* I am liking) (*or* I do like)	amāmus	we like (*or* we are liking) (*or* we do like)
2nd Person	amās	you (s.) like (*or* you are liking) (*or* you do like)	amātis	you (pl.) like (*or* you are liking) (*or* you do like)
3rd Person	amat	he (she, it) likes (*or* he is liking) (*or* he does like)	amant	they like (*or* they are liking) (*or* they do like)

First Declension

A Latin noun belongs to the first declension if the genitive singular ends in -ae. Remove the -ae from the genitive singular to find the stem. These nouns are usually feminine, unless they describe males in Latin culture such as sailors, poets, or farmers.

	Singular	Meaning	Plural	Meaning
Nominative	puella	a girl (*or* the girl)	puellae	girls (*or* the girls)
Genitive	puellae	of a girl (*or* of the girl)	puellārum	of girls (*or* of the girls)
Dative	puellae	to/for a girl (*or* to/for the girl)	puellīs	to/for girls (*or* to/for the girls)
Accusative	puellam	a girl (*or* the girl)	puellās	girls (*or* the girls)
Ablative	puellā	by/with* a girl (*or* by/with* the girl)	puellīs	by/with* girls (*or* by/with* the girls)

*The translations given above are just a sampling of the many possible meanings of the ablative case.

APPENDIX

Second Declension

A Latin noun belongs to the second declension if the genitive singular ends in -ī. Remove the -ī from the genitive singular to find the stem. If a second declension nominative ends in -us, it is usually masculine.

	Singular	*Meaning*	*Plural*	*Meaning*
Nominative	amīcus	a friend (*or* the friend)	amīcī	friends (*or* the friends)
Genitive	amīcī	of a friend (*or* of the friend)	amīcōrum	of friends (*or* of the friends)
Dative	amīcō	to/for a friend (*or* to/for the friend)	amīcīs	to/for friends (*or* to/for the friends)
Accusative	amīcum	a friend (*or* the friend)	amīcōs	friends (*or* the friends)
Ablative	amīcō	by/with* a friend (*or* by/with* the friend)	amīcīs	by/with* friends (*or* by/with* the friends)

*The translations given above are just a sampling of the many possible meanings of the ablative case.

Second Declension -ius

A Latin second declension -ius noun is declined like a second declension -us noun except in the genitive singular. The expected genitive singular -iī of these -ius nouns is shortened to -ī. However, the stem retains the -i- [soci-].

	Singular	*Meaning*	*Plural*	*Meaning*
Nominative	socius	an ally (*or* the ally)	sociī	allies (*or* the allies)
Genitive	socī	of an ally (*or* of the ally)	sociōrum	of allies (*or* of the allies)
Dative	sociō	to/for an ally (*or* to/for the ally)	sociīs	to/for allies (*or* to/for the allies)
Accusative	socium	an ally (*or* the ally)	sociōs	allies (*or* the allies)
Ablative	sociō	by/with* an ally (*or* by/with* the ally)	sociīs	by/with* allies (*or* by/with* the allies)

*The translations given above are just a sampling of the many possible meanings of the ablative case.

178

APPENDIX

Index

APPENDIX

Flashcard Tips

1. Remember to practice flashcards daily.

2. Do not move ahead in the workbook if your student is struggling for mastery. Review the flashcards every day until your student is confident and ready to learn more.

3. For each noun and verb ending, there are some "example" words to help your student become familiar with the endings. Please help your student apply these endings to all vocabulary words.

4. When the number of cards becomes too cumbersome to do in one day, remove the cards your student knows without hesitation and put them in an "Occasional Practice" stack. Review the "Occasional Practice" stack once a week.

"Latin's Not So Tough!"
Level Three
Feedback Form

Dear Friend of Greek 'n' Stuff:

Please use the following form to give us your feedback regarding this workbook. Mail your comments to:

> Greek 'n' Stuff
> P.O. Box 882
> Moline, IL 61266-0882

If you prefer, you may send your comments via fax (309-796-2706).

What did you enjoy about this book?

_____

_____

_____

_____

In what ways could this book be more effective?

_____

_____

_____

_____

Circle "yes" beside the Learning Aids which you found helpful in your studies. We would also like to know what you especially liked about each (and/or any suggestions you may have for improvement).

yes   "Answers Only" key _____

yes   "Full Text" key _____

yes   Quizzes/Exams _____

yes   "Flashcards on a Ring" _____

yes   Pronunciation CD/tape _____

yes   Greek 'n' Stuff's Internet homepage (**www.greeknstuff.com**) with its "Greek and Latin Words of the Month" _____

(front)	(back)
puella *put*	(Start on page 11.) (Level 3) **girl** as in The girl sees the son.
vocō	(Page 11) (Level 3) I call as in I call the son.
puer	(Page 11) (Level 3) **boy** as in The boy sees the son.
dō	(Page 11) (Level 3) I give, I grant as in I give the trumpet.
agricola	(Page 12) (Level 3) farmer as in The farmer sees the son.
aqua	(Page 12) (Level 3) water as in The water is in the farmhouse.

(front)	(back)
est	(Page 12) (Level 3) **he is, she is, it is, there is** as in <u>He is</u> the son.
fēmina	(Page 12) (Level 3) **woman, wife** as in <u>The woman</u> sees the son.
et	(Page 13) (Level 3) **and, also, even** as in The boy sees the son <u>and</u> the daughter.
silva	(Page 13) (Level 3) **forest** as in <u>The forest</u> is on the island.
īnsula	(Page 13) (Level 3) **island** as in <u>The island</u> is in the water.
sunt	(Page 13) (Level 3) **they are, there are** as in <u>They are</u> the sons.

(front)	(back)
laudō	(Page 14) (Level 3) **I praise** as in <u>I praise</u> the son.
nōn	(Page 14) (Level 3) **not** as in I do <u>not</u> praise the son.
ad	(Page 14) (Level 3) **to, near, toward, for, at** as in The ship sails <u>to</u> the island.
vīta	(Page 14) (Level 3) **life** as in <u>Life</u> is short.
porta	(Page 15) (Level 3) **gate** as in <u>The gate</u> is open.
memoria	(Page 15) (Level 3) **memory** as in <u>The memory</u> of the horse is vivid.

(front)	(back)
nāvigō	(Page 15) (Level 3) **I sail** as in <u>I sail</u> to the island.
sed	(Page 15) (Level 3) **but** as in I see the son, <u>but</u> I do not see the daughter.
fortūna	(Page 16) (Level 3) **fortune, chance, luck** as in <u>The fortune</u> of the son seemed bad.
via	(Page 16) (Level 3) **road, way, street** as in <u>The road</u> is wide.
portō	(Page 16) (Level 3) **I carry** as in <u>I carry</u> the trumpet.
quid	(Page 16) (Level 3) **what** (a question) as in <u>What</u> is in the wagon?

(front)	(back)
tuba	(Page 17) (Level 3) **trumpet** as in <u>The trumpet</u> is loud.
ager	(Page 17) (Level 3) **field, territory** as in <u>The field</u> is green.
parō	(Page 17) (Level 3) **I prepare, I prepare for** as in <u>I prepare</u> the horses.
amīcus	(Page 17) (Level 3) **friend** as in <u>The friend</u> is kind.
spectō	(Page 19) (Level 3) **I look at** as in <u>I look at</u> the field.
nātūra	(Page 19) (Level 3) **nature** as in <u>The nature</u> of the horse is wild.

(front)	(back)
campus	(Page 19) field, plain (Level 3) as in The plain is level.
occupō	(Page 19) I seize, I capture (Level 3) as in I seize the island.
cum	(Page 20) along with, with (Level 3) as in He fights with boldness.
nauta	(Page 20) sailor (Level 3) as in The sailor sees the son.
vīlla	(Page 20) farmhouse, country house, villa (Level 3) as in The farmhouse is in the country.
littera	(Page 20) letter (Level 3) (of the alphabet) (if plural: epistle, letter) as in The letter looks like an *a*.

(front)	(back)
ubi	(Page 21) (Level 3) **where** (a question) as in _Where_ is the son?
fīlius	(Page 21) (Level 3) **son** as in _The son_ sees the daughter.
patria	(Page 21) (Level 3) **country,** **native land** as in _The native land_ is beautiful.
fīlia	(Page 21) (Level 3) **daughter** as in _The daughter_ sees the son.
amīcitia	(Page 22) (Level 3) **friendliness,** **friendship** as in _The friendliness_ of the son is known.
amō	(Page 22) (Level 3) **I love,** **I like** as in _I love_ the son.

(front)	(back)
lingua	(Page 22) (Level 3) **tongue, language** as in <u>The language</u> of the people is known.
equus	(Page 22) (Level 3) **horse** as in <u>The horse</u> sees the son.
poēta	(Page 23) (Level 3) **poet** as in <u>The poet</u> sees the son.
annus	(Page 23) (Level 3) **year** as in <u>The year</u> passes quickly.
pugnō	(Page 23) (Level 3) **I fight** as in <u>I fight</u> the son.
terra	(Page 23) (Level 3) **earth, land, country** as in <u>The land</u> is rocky.

(front)	(back)
gladius	(Page 24)　　　　　(Level 3) sword as in The sword belongs to the son.
prōvincia	(Page 24)　　　　　(Level 3) province as in The province belongs to the queen.
puellam	(Page 27)　　　　　(Level 3) girl as in I like the girl.
fīlium	(Page 27)　　　　　(Level 3) son as in I like the son.
amīcum	(Page 27)　　　　　(Level 3) friend as in I like the friend.
puellās	(Page 31)　　　　　(Level 3) girls as in I like the girls.

(front)	(back)
fīliōs	(Page 31) · (Level 3) **sons** as in I like <u>the sons</u>.
amīcōs	(Page 31) · (Level 3) **friends** as in I like <u>the friends</u>.
amāmus	(Page 35) · (Level 3) **we love, we like** as in <u>We like</u> the son.
portāmus	(Page 35) · (Level 3) **we carry** as in <u>We carry</u> the trumpet.
(genitive singular) **puellae**	(Page 39) · (Level 3) **of the girl** as in I like the farmhouse <u>of the girl</u>.
fīlī	(Page 39) · (Level 3) **of the son** as in I like the farmhouse <u>of the son</u>.

(front)	(back)
(genitive singular) ## amīcī	(Page 39)　　　(Level 3) ### of the friend as in I like the farmhouse <u>of the friend</u>.
## lēgātus	(Page 43)　　　(Level 3) ### lieutenant, envoy as in <u>The lieutenant</u> sees the son.
## lūdus	(Page 43)　　　(Level 3) ### game, play, school as in <u>The game</u> is over.
## appellō	(Page 43)　　　(Level 3) ### I address, I call, I name as in <u>I address</u> the son.
## servus	(Page 45)　　　(Level 3) ### slave as in <u>The slave</u> sees the son.
## nūntius	(Page 45)　　　(Level 3) ### messenger, message, news as in <u>The messenger</u> sees the son.

(front)	(back)
nūntiō	(Page 45) (Level 3) **I announce,** **I report** as in I announce the news.
nārrō	(Page 47) (Level 3) **I relate,** **I tell** as in I tell the story.
fāma	(Page 47) (Level 3) **report, rumor,** **reputation** as in The report is hard to believe.
populus	(Page 47) (Level 3) **people,** **nation, tribe** as in The people love the son.
rēgīna	(Page 49) (Level 3) **queen** as in The queen sees the son.
exspectō	(Page 49) (Level 3) **I await,** **I wait for** as in I await the son.

(front)	(back)
epistula	(Page 49) (Level 3) **letter, epistle** as in The letter brings good news.
habitō	(Page 51) (Level 3) **I live, I dwell** as in I live on the island.
nunc	(Page 51) (Level 3) **now** as in The son now sees the daughter.
fābula	(Page 51) (Level 3) **story** as in The story ended happily.
dēlectō	(Page 53) (Level 3) **I please** as in I please the son.
labōrō	(Page 53) (Level 3) **I labor, I suffer, I am hard pressed** as in I labor in the fields.

(front)	(back)
causa	(Page 53) (Level 3) cause, reason as in The cause of the battle is known.
socius	(Page 55) (Level 3) comrade, ally as in The comrade sees the son.
dīligentia	(Page 55) (Level 3) diligence, care as in The diligence of the son is pleasing.
convocō	(Page 55) (Level 3) I call together, I assemble, I summon as in I assemble the sons of the province.
puellārum	(Page 67) (Level 3) of the girls as in I like the farmhouse of the girls.
fīliōrum	(Page 67) (Level 3) of the sons as in I like the farmhouse of the sons.

(front)	(back)
amīcōrum	(Page 67) (Level 3) **of the friends** as in I like the farmhouse <u>of the friends.</u>
amat	(Page 71) (Level 3) **he (she, it) loves, he (she, it) likes** as in <u>He likes</u> the son.
portat	(Page 71) (Level 3) **he carries** as in <u>He carries</u> the trumpet.
amant	(Page 79) (Level 3) **they love, they like** as in <u>They like</u> the son.
portant	(Page 79) (Level 3) **they carry** as in <u>They carry</u> the trumpet.
(nominative plural) puellae	(Page 83) (Level 3) **girls** as in <u>The girls</u> see the sons.

(front)	(back)
fīliī	(Page 83)　　　　　(Level 3) **sons** as in <u>The sons</u> see the girls.
(nominative plural) **amīcī**	(Page 83)　　　　　(Level 3) **friends** as in <u>The friends</u> see the son.
superō	(Page 93)　　　　　(Level 3) **I surpass, I defeat** as in <u>I surpass</u> the sailors.
cōpia	(Page 93)　　　　　(Level 3) **plenty, supply** as in <u>The supply</u> of water is gone.
in	(Page 93)　　　　　(Level 3) **into, against, in, on** as in I swim <u>in</u> the water.
oppugnō	(Page 95)　　　　　(Level 3) **I attack** as in <u>I attack</u> the queen's enemies.

(front)	(back)
diū	(Page 95) (Level 3) **long,** **for a long time** as in We waited at the gate <u>for a long time</u>.
vulnerō	(Page 95) (Level 3) **I wound** as in <u>I wound</u> the son.
fuga	(Page 97) (Level 3) **flight,** **exile** as in <u>The exile</u> of the nation caused sorrow.
iam	(Page 97) (Level 3) **now,** **already** as in The son is <u>already</u> here.
temptō	(Page 97) (Level 3) **I try,** **I attempt** as in <u>I attempt</u> to climb the mountain.
herī	(Page 99) (Level 3) **yesterday** as in I saw the son <u>yesterday</u>.

(front)	(back)
servō	(Page 99) (Level 3) **I guard, I save, I keep** as in <u>I guard</u> the son with a sword.
poēna	(Page 99) (Level 3) **penalty, punishment** as in <u>The penalty</u> for theft is harsh.
semper	(Page 101) (Level 3) **always** as in I will <u>always</u> love the son.
captīvus	(Page 101) (Level 3) **captive** as in <u>The captive</u> sees the son.
locus	(Page 101) (Level 3) **place, location, situation** as in <u>The location</u> of the house is near the lake.
audācia	(Page 103) (Level 3) **boldness, daring** as in <u>The boldness</u> of the son was unexpected.

(front)	(back)
hodiē	(Page 103) (Level 3) **today** as in The son sees the daughter <u>today</u>.
volō	(Page 103) (Level 3) **I fly** as in <u>I fly</u> like a bird.
animus	(Page 105) (Level 3) **mind,** **spirit** as in <u>The mind</u> of the son is sharp.
crās	(Page 105) (Level 3) **tomorrow** as in The son will see the daughter <u>tomorrow</u>.
carrus	(Page 105) (Level 3) **cart,** **wagon** as in <u>The cart</u> carries the boxes.
amās	(Page 117) (Level 3) **you love,** **you like** (only one "you") as in <u>You like</u> the son.

(front)	(back)
portās	(Page 117) (Level 3) **you carry** (only one "you") as in _You carry_ the trumpet.
*(ablative of **place where** singular)* **in īnsulā**	(Page 121) (Level 3) **on the island** as in The girl lives _on the island_.
*(ablative of **place where** singular)* **in lūdō**	(Page 121) (Level 3) **in the school** as in The girl lives _in the school_.
*(ablative of **place where** plural)* **in īnsulīs**	(Page 123) (Level 3) **on the islands** as in The girl lives _on the islands_.
*(ablative of **place where** plural)* **in lūdīs**	(Page 123) (Level 3) **in the schools** as in The girl lives _in the schools_.
*(ablative of **means or instrument** singular)* **tubā**	(Page 125) (Level 3) **on the trumpet** ("by means of") as in I summon the girls _on the trumpet_.

(front)	(back)
*(ablative of **means or instrument** plural)* # tubīs	(Page 125) (Level 3) ## on the trumpets ("by means of") as in I summon the girls <u>on the trumpets</u>.
*(ablative of **manner**)* # cum audāciā	(Page 127) (Level 3) ## with boldness (the **manner** in which a thing is done) as in I fight <u>with boldness</u>.
# amātis	(Page 129) (Level 3) ## you love, you like (more than one "you") as in <u>You like</u> the son.
# portātis	(Page 129) (Level 3) ## you carry (more than one "you") as in <u>You carry</u> the trumpets.
(dative singular) # puellae	(Page 133) (Level 3) ## to (or for) the girl as in I give the cart <u>to the girl</u>.
(dative singular) # fīliō	(Page 133) (Level 3) ## to (or for) the son as in I give the cart <u>to the son</u>.

(front)	(back)
(dative singular) amīcō	(Page 133) (Level 3) to (or for) the friend as in I give the cart <u>to the friend</u>.
(dative plural) puellīs	(Page 137) (Level 3) to (or for) the girls as in I give the cart <u>to the girls</u>.
(dative plural) fīliīs	(Page 137) (Level 3) to (or for) the sons as in I give the cart <u>to the sons</u>.
(dative plural) amīcīs	(Page 137) (Level 3) to (or for) the friends as in I give the cart <u>to the friends</u>.
cūra	(Page 141) (Level 3) care, anxiety as in <u>The anxiety</u> of the soldier is great.
stō	(Page 141) (Level 3) I stand as in <u>I stand</u> at the gate.

(front)	(back)
saepe	(Page 141) (Level 3) **often** as in The son <u>often</u> sees the daughter.
lībero	(Page 143) (Level 3) **I set free, I free** as in <u>I free</u> the captives.
interim	(Page 143) (Level 3) **meanwhile** as in <u>Meanwhile</u> the son sees the daughter.
cūr	(Page 143) (Level 3) **why** (a question) as in <u>Why</u> does the son see the daughter?
dēmōnstrō	(Page 145) (Level 3) **I point out, I show** as in <u>I show</u> the trumpet to the son.
hōra	(Page 145) (Level 3) **hour** as in <u>The hour</u> of the meeting has come.

(front)	(back)
posteā	(Page 145) (Level 3) **after that time,** **afterward, thereafter** as in <u>Afterward</u> the son blew the trumpet.
inopia	(Page 147) (Level 3) **want, lack,** **need, poverty** as in The <u>poverty</u> of the tribe is alarming.
pecūnia	(Page 147) (Level 3) **wealth,** **money** as in The <u>money</u> is in the box.
cōnfīrmō	(Page 147) (Level 3) **I strengthen,** **I encourage, I declare** as in <u>I encourage</u> the son's boldness.
tum	(Page 149) (Level 3) **then,** **at that time** as in The poet wrote the book <u>at that time</u>.
clāmō	(Page 149) (Level 3) **I shout** as in <u>I shout</u> the news to the people.

(front)	(back)
dominus	(Page 149) (Level 3) master, Lord, owner as in <u>The master</u> sees the son.
ambulō	(Page 151) (Level 3) I stroll, I walk as in <u>I stroll</u> through the forest.
male	(Page 151) (Level 3) badly, insufficiently as in The soldier fought <u>badly</u>.
numerus	(Page 151) (Level 3) number, group as in <u>The group</u> of children play the game.